SINISTER HANDS AND PEACHTREE MIRACLES

SINISTER HANDS AND PEACHTREE MIRACLES

A Memoir

ESSIE KNOWLES FISCHER

The Creative Visionaries, LLC

ISBN:

978-0-578-88418-9 (Paperback)

978-0-578-88637-4 (eBook)

Dedication

My Mother
The late Nemoia (Naomi) Jackson
I love you for bringing me into this world and wish I could
have had the opportunity to know you.

My Great Uncle and Aunt—Adoptive Parents
The late Robert Blakemore Knowles
The late Sophia Wesley Knowles
I love you both beyond words and thank God constantly for
blessing me with you as my parents. I could not have asked for
more.

My Son and Daughter and their spouses
My Eight Grandchildren
My Great Granddaughter
The joys of my life! After God, family is everything. I love you
all so much!

Abuse victims who have not only survived but thrived.

Contents

ONE

Michael's Recollection

I *f I remember correctly, the first time I became aware of the nightmares was the night Dad and I were camping deep in the woods near Mammoth Lakes in the Sierra Nevada Mountains in California. It was around two or three in the morning and eerily quiet. A sliver of moonlight peeked through the slit of the tent's opening, casting a dagger-like shadow across the floor that moved up and down as the wind whipped against the tent's flap covering. For whatever reason, I could not sleep and had been tossing and turning for what seemed like an eternity. All of a sudden, I heard this whimpering sound, almost like an injured animal. I jumped, then held my breath and tried to lie as still as possible.*

Was it a wolf? A coyote? A bear? After a minute, I quietly sat up, trying not to make a sound as I began fishing for the flashlight. Turning my head slightly and leaning forward, I thought I heard it again, except this time, it sounded like the animal was inside the tent. My heart started pounding in my chest, and I leaned over to try to touch Dad to quietly wake him up, when all of a sudden, the tent exploded with the most other-worldly sound I had ever heard. It was as though it had rattled up from the bowels of the earth, starting low and crescendo-ing to a pitch that was glass-shattering.

"Owww ... ee ... oww ... ch ... h-elp, please ... you're hurting me ... stop, S t o p! Don't hurt me ... I didn't do it ... I didn't do nothing, please, leave me alone ... no ... please ... not the cigarette ... no ... no ... S-T-O-P!"

"Dad! Dad, wake up!" I screamed, shaking him as hard as I could.

He bolted upright, drenched in sweat and shaking so violently that it scared me to death.

"Dad, what's wrong? Dad, talk to me!" I yelled as tears welled in my eyes and flowed down my face.

That was the first time I experienced one of Dad's all-consuming nightmares, but there would be more, many more. As I was growing up, I would ask him about them, but he just refused to talk about it or reveal what they stemmed from. My sisters and I knew he suffered from them quite a bit. There would be mornings when we were getting ready for school that Dad would come out of his bedroom with dark circles under his eyes, attesting to the fact that he probably hadn't slept at all. My sisters and I would sometimes hear his screams through the walls or our mom yelling trying to wake him up. Sometimes after those terrible nightmares, Dad would sit at the table and just stare into space for long periods of time. At those times, he would become irritated if we tried to talk to him or ask him questions. A couple of times, I saw him sitting there wiping tears away but trying to hide the fact that he was crying.

Then, there was this incident that left an indelible imprint on my heart. It was Dad's birthday. His mother, father, some of his friends, my mom, sisters, and I had gathered in the back room of one of our local restaurants. After we had sung "Happy Birthday" and he had blown out the candles, Nanna, Dad's mother, started to share some memories of Dad with us. Midway through her presentation, Dad suddenly jumped up and ran from the room, screaming something about him wishing he had never been born. He continued yelling, "Why did she abandon me? Why? Wasn't I good enough to be her son? What the hell is wrong with me anyway that nobody wanted me and just threw me away like an abandoned dog?" his voice fading as he got farther and farther away.

We all sat there in stunned silence, bewildered, holding our breath, afraid to move or look at each other. No one dared utter a single word.

There was also the mystery of a couple of round scars on Dad's arm that looked different from the long scar on his forehead where he had run into the corner of the fireplace or the two oblong-like ones on his leg from old football injuries. When I asked how he got them, a cloud came over his face as he said absentmindedly, "They were punishment for me doing something wrong." Beyond that bit of information, he gave no other explanation. As far as Dad was concerned, the case was closed. Instinct told me that it was far too painful to talk about.

As I grew older, I often wondered what demons were wreaking havoc with his life. When had it all started? What horrors had he experienced in his life that caused him to be constantly plagued with these nightmares? What triggered them?

Now, years later as I sit listening to my psychology professor discuss the guidelines for our end-of-the-year research project that will deal with "Understanding Human Behavior in the Social Environment," I reflect back to my dad. Would this project provide the perfect opportunity to delve into Dad's past? Even better, would it be a good time to talk to Nanna Bee, who we simply call Nanna, and see what light she could shed on his background, especially after his outburst at his birthday party? Children always want to know their history, where they come from, information about their roots. Then, too, there seemed to be a mystery surrounding Nanna Bee's childhood. I can vaguely remember her hinting at some horrific things she went through as a baby and a little girl that helped prepare her for raising Dad. Just like him, though, she volunteered very little information when pressed. In fact, once she started to cry uncontrollably after my sisters and I kept begging her to tell us more about it. Now, I'm beginning to wonder, What skeletons lie deeply hidden in the Ferguson closet?

In making my decision to take on this project, I must consider both the upside and downside, and that brings to mind a million questions. Will I be opening up a can of worms or a Pandora's Box as I begin to explore and expose? What will come out? What evil acts lie hidden beneath the bones in the basement? Will I make it worse? Will Dad be willing to divulge the secrets he has kept hidden for so many years? Will my probing send him deeper into depression or will this be liberating for him? Do I dare take this chance? Will this forever change my relationship with and my feelings for my dad? So many questions and very little guidance as to whether I should or should not begin the search to find the answers. If I move ahead, will I find myself traveling down the freeway at a high rate of speed, going in the wrong direction and destroying everything in my path?

TWO

Starting a New Life Together

NORTH LITTLE ROCK, ARKANSAS–FEBRUARY 1933

Neiomi could not remember when she had been happier. Looking lovingly up into the eyes of Lewis Anthony Wilson, she struggled to keep her voice steady and tears of joy from rolling down her cheeks. She took a deep breath and squeezed his hands as Pastor Nichols asked her to repeat after him. "I, Neiomi Elaine, take thee, Lewis Anthony, to be my lawful husband, to have and to hold from this day forward … until death do us part."

Neiomi felt her heart would burst as her new husband leaned over and gave her a tender, lingering kiss. Caught up in the excitement of the moment, any traces of the huge fight she had had with some of her siblings and other family members a couple of hours ago were all but forgotten. She wasn't going to let anything or anybody ruin her special day.

For several weeks now, Neiomi's brothers had been nagging and begging her not to marry Lewis, or Lou as he was called by his family and the folk who knew him. She had been hurt by her oldest brother storming out of the room and saying he would not give her away to that skirt-chasing guitar player. Nonetheless, her sister, also against her marrying Lou, came through and stood beside Neiomi during the ceremony. Now, she was Mrs. Lewis Anthony Wilson! She was on cloud nine!

Everybody seemed to be up in a stew about her and Lou only knowing each other a few months, but that didn't matter to her. She loved him with all her heart, and for the first time in her life, she was being treated like a real lady. Lord knows she sure needed a good man who would treat her right because that dog of a man she was married to before was just a no-good bum. He'd up and left her with no money and two baby boys to raise by herself. She heard he had run off with some other woman. It was hard for a while as she struggled for a place to live and to keep food on the table, but now that was all behind her. She was married again and looking forward to a good, long, happy life.

Lou was the most handsome man she had ever courted, and he had a real knack for playing that guitar. In fact, everybody around wanted to hear him play. He was used to being asked to play for smaller crowds around North Little Rock and in Keo and England, Arkansas, which was only about an hour's drive south. Lately, though, he was being booked to play for shows as far away as Eudora and even in Memphis, which took about four hours to reach, each in different directions. Before the wedding, he had even invited her to go along with him a couple of times; and she was so proud to sit and watch him play and have him introduce her as his lady or his "Honey Cake," as he fondly referred to her.

One time, though, when she had gone with him, she

noticed that women were hanging on to him and were all up in his face trying to talk to him. Neiomi started to get upset but tried not to let it show or act like it bothered her since she didn't want to look like a jealous girlfriend. She knew he loved her because he always told her so and treated her real special. He even brought her flowers once, and she still had them. Before they had died, she'd taken and hung them upside down in a corner of her bedroom. They were still hanging there, and she promised herself she was going to take them with her wherever she went. Every time she looked at them, they brought a big ole smile to her face. At night when she was lonely, she would look at them before going to sleep because they reminded her that Lou really loved her. No man, excepting for Lou, had ever brought her flowers.

Neiomi had been upset right before the wedding because of the warnings her sister and brothers kept giving her. "You don't need to be marrying no man you haven't known but just a few months, and besides, I hear he's nothing but a 'rolling stone' and a skirt chaser. You've already been done wrong by one no-good husband, so why you want to go and get another one?" She had to admit that she was taken by surprise when Lou first asked her to marry him after they had only been courting several months. She thought he was just playing a joke on her at first, but he wouldn't give up. He kept hounding her and hounding her until she finally said, "Yes."

When they first got married, Lou was working at Odell's Lumber Mill in North Little Rock, and they had gotten a little place to live over on Sixth Street. But times were hard, other stores were closing, and people just didn't have the money to spend, so they had to let him go a month after the wedding.

They tried to make it on their own for a few weeks but were forced to move in with Estella, Neiomi's sister. Lou tried day and night but couldn't find a job. The only money they had was the money Lou got from playing at different places around town. Every once in a while, he was able to travel an hour or so down the road to Pine Bluff, but with his old Model T Ford breaking down every other week now, he just wasn't able to go too far anymore.

One night, Lou was playing at Joe's Chicken and Rib Place in North Little Rock. Joe's was one of the few places where Lou played for white folks. During his break, he over-heard a guy talking about the owner of Johnston Sharecrop-ping Plantation looking for folks to come and rent a plot of farmland and work it. Lou bided his time, and when the guy was alone, went up and told him he had lost his job a while back and was looking for a way to make money to take care of his family. The guy introduced himself as Jim, shook Lou's hand, and told him he was really enjoying the music. He then began giving Lou more information about the Johnston Plantation.

"You see, Owner Ben Johnston has about a hundred acres of farmland that's been in his family since the mid-1800s. They used to have slaves working the plantation, but after the slaves were freed, he's had to find a way to get some help since he can't work it by himself. So, Ben decided to do what a lot of plantation owners are doing around here. He's divided his property up into different sized farming plots and renting them out. For folks interested in renting a plot, he lets them work the land, and then when harvest time rolls around, the renters give him a share of the profit they get. The percentage of profit the renters owe him depends on a few things. If the renter has the money to buy his own seed, fertilizer, tools, and such, then Ben gets about twenty-five percent of the profit. But most tenants don't have the money to buy that stuff up front, so Ben extends credit that allows them to buy everything they need to get started. He has a little store right on the plantation called the commissary where you can get almost everything you need including food and clothing. Once your harvest comes in, you can then pay off your bill at the commissary as well. Another good thing about sharecropping on the Johnston Plantation is that Ben gives you and your family a place to live, and there's even a primary school your kids can attend. This just might be what you're looking for, Lou."

"Yes, sir," Lou responded, trying not to seem too excited but also thinking, *This may be just what I need to get out of the God-forsaken house with Neiomi's sister.* "Can you tell me how to get to this Johnston Plantation?" Lou continued.

"Sure can," answered Jim. "You go out here to Highway 165 and head east for about fifteen or so miles. You'll know you're in Scott when you see the old Watson Grain Mill on your right. Just past the mill, you'll come up on a dirt road on the right. Turn there and drive just a little piece in, and you'll come up on a big white house on the left. That's where Ben Johnston lives. You can go in and talk to him if you're thinking about renting a plot to work. I'll warn you, though, it's hard work, and folk who are tenant farmers working as sharecroppers say you work from dawn to dusk, or as the locals so famously put it, you work from 'kin see to kain't see.' Jim paused, rubbed his chin, and chuckled, then continued, "But if you think this kind of set up can help you, go on out to Scott and talk to ole Ben. I hope though that you're not gonna stop playing that guitar of yours here at Joe's because, man, you're really good with that thing."

Oh, no sir, no–o–o sir!" Lou quickly put in. "I'm gonna keep on playing because playing is what I like doing most of all. I just need to do something else to put a roof over our heads and food on the table for me and my family."

So now, almost four months to the day they were married, Neiomi and Lou were moving into a tenant house on Johnston Plantation. Neiomi hated moving away from her family, especially her sister, whom she and the boys had lived with for a period of time after her first husband had left them and while she was trying to get on her feet. However, Lou had been looking for a way to take care of his growing family and thought the idea of sharecropping was a good one. Besides, Scott was only about a thirty-minute drive from North Little Rock, so Neiomi could always make the trip up to see her family, or they could make the short trek to Scott.

During the drive to Scott, Lou explained the terms of the lease he had worked out with Mr. Johnston. "Neiomi, we got us ten acres of farmland that we can either plant cotton, corn, or tobacco on. I'm thinking cotton'll be better for us because it'll get us more money. We have to pay Ole Man Johnston a third of what we make on the crop, but I don't think that's too bad. Since we don't have a mule or seed or any tools to work the farm, Mr. Johnston is gonna let us get the stuff we need on credit. He said that'll probably come to about another third of our profit. I know it's a lot, but we don't have a choice right now. At least we have a house to live in and a plantation store where we can get the food and stuff we need to make it to harvest time. I know we can do this, and remember, I can still play my guitar some nights and make money too." Neiomi wasn't too excited about the idea but knew Lou was really trying to make a good life for her and the kids, so she promised herself she would do everything she possibly could to make this sharecropping thing work.

Once Lou's old car turned off Highway 165 and onto the road leading to their new home, Neiomi thought the car would fall apart from the shaking as it hit rut after rut. Lou pointed to the ten-acre farming plot on the right and said, "Neiomi, that's the land we're gonna farm! We really got to hustle because planting season is almost done. I think, though, that we can still get a good crop in before harvest time. We all just have to work hard." They drove on for a few more minutes, and just as they rounded the bend, Lou said excitedly as he pointed, "There's our new home!"

Neiomi, who had been looking at their farming plot and wondering how on earth they were going to get all that planting done with just her, Lou, and the two little boys, turned and looked to where Lou was pointing. Her heart fell to the floor. Lou had warned her that the place needed some work, but this house needed way more than just some work. It was a mess! "Oh my Lord, Lou, the house is kinda leaning to one side and looks like somebody tried to patch up the roof by putting pieces of tin over where the shingles came off," Neiomi said before realizing Lou may take it as a criticism, and she sure didn't want to sound ungrateful or say something that would be discouraging.

Surprisingly, he agreed. "Yeah, we'll have to get busy fixing it up, but at least we got us a house of our own and don't have to be depending on your folks to take care of us." Neiomi nodded in agreement but secretly wondered how they were going to plant ten acres of cotton and get the house fixed up too.

The house looked like it had been built a hundred years ago, and that nobody had done much to it since it was built. Neiomi had to admit the logs looked sturdy enough, even if they were weather beaten and had this ugly grayish color. There were a few logs where the chinking had come out, so you could see right through to the inside of the house. That sure needed to be fixed before winter. As for the two round concrete blocks on the left side, it looked like the ground had given away. This made the blocks tip outward and caused the house to lean slightly to the left. There really wasn't much they would do about that but just pray that the ground was done shifting.

The inside of the house looked pretty much like she imagined it would after having seen the outside. There were four rooms all total, and each room was directly behind the other. She said to Lou, "I've never been in a house before where you can stand at the front door and look straight through to the back door."

Lou quickly responded, "Oh yeah, they call this kind of house a shotgun house, because if you stand at the front door and fire a shotgun, the bullet will go straight through the house and out the backdoor without hitting a wall."

The front room had a tiny window that looked out onto the front porch but could not be opened, so the room was dark and drab as well as hot and stuffy when the door was closed. The folks who had lived there before had left an old broken-down settee, which Neiomi decided they would use to sit on for now, but would get rid of just as soon as they received their money from the first harvest. Until then, they would just have to make do. The second and third rooms each had a larger window on the left side of the house, which made it a little better to get fresh air and sunlight. She liked the second room as their bedroom and decided the kids would have the bedroom next to the kitchen. That way, they would not have to trek through her and Lou's bedroom to go to the kitchen to get some water or out back to the outhouse. This arrangement would give them a little more privacy. There was also an old iron bed in the second room that she and Lou would share, but no furniture at all was in the third room. She would just have to make pallets on the floor for now. Thank goodness her sister had given her several old quilts that the kids could use to sleep on. They would have to find beds for them before winter rolled around because it would be way too cold for them to sleep on the floor.

Neiomi liked the kitchen the best. This was the brightest room in the house with a window facing west toward the back of the house. In the corner was an orange-like or rust-colored three-burner cast-iron wood-burning stove. The stove had a flue pipe that ran all the way up through the roof to let out the smoke. She especially liked the color, and even though it was faded in places, it brightened up the room and made it feel warm and cozy. The tenants before them had left a few tin plates, a brownish water jug with a faded John S…OS label on the front, and a tin cup sitting on the bottom shelf of an old paint-chipped white cabinet with two broken doors. A cooking pot, bucket, and a number two tin tub used for washing both dishes and clothes hung on nails on the wall that ran next to the stove. The table consisted of two planks placed on top of two wooden horses. Two wooden straight-back chairs, one with a broken leg, sat against the back wall. Walking past the chairs and out the back door, Neiomi saw a small patch of land to the left of the little back porch where she figured she could plant a small garden and have fresh vegetables for her family. She might even have enough to share with neighbors if they were going through a hard time. An old water pump stood about ten feet away, so getting water for the house and garden wouldn't be too much of a problem.

It wasn't a lot, but Neiomi knew she could make it work. The kitchen would be the main room where her family would enjoy good suppers together, talk about what happened during the day, share good news, and give comforting hugs when the news was not so good. Here, they could be a real family, and it would feel like home. She would fix all the special foods that Lou liked. For the first time since they had pulled away from Estella's house that morning, a big smile came across her face. Light coming through the kitchen window highlighted a pair of big brown eyes that sparkled in the sun and the hint of a dimple on her right cheek. Yes, here on Johnston's Plantation, her, Lou, and the kids were going to have a good life together. Neiomi just knew it in her heart.

THREE

Fatal Attraction

JULY 11, 1941

Lucy flung the empty, tattered burlap sack into the back of her old red Chevy pickup truck, climbed in, and with shaky fingers started the engine. She took several deep breaths trying to calm her nerves and racing heart, saying aloud, "I'm not gonna let nerves get the best of me now!" For weeks, she had spent restless days and sleepless nights concocting her plan. Now, she was just about twenty-four hours away from successfully carrying it out, and she was not about to let nerves and feelings of guilt creep in and get in her way.

Within five minutes of leaving her house, she had come to the end of the dirt road that ran from her place to the main highway. Lucy tapped her fingers anxiously as she waited for a car to pass, then turned right onto Arkansas State Highway 165, heading west toward North Little Rock. Her first stop would be Terkel's Feed and Supply Store. There, she would get the most important item she would need for her plan.

Several minutes later, nerves had quieted down, and she was in control again. At that moment, had anyone else been riding in the truck and paying attention, they would have noticed a transformation of Lucy's face as it contorted into something almost unrecognizable. She was consumed with thoughts of what she was about to do and all the pleasures she would enjoy once her plan had succeeded.

Twenty minutes later, Lucy was pulling up in front of Terkel's. She had to go down the street a piece before being able to park the truck. Seemed like every farmer in Pulaski County was there getting something or other even though it was still early in the day. There were several feed and supply stores in North Little Rock, but Terkel's was the most popular because of the wide variety of supplies they carried; plus, the price was a bit cheaper than the other stores. Old man Terkel was always on hand to answer any questions the older farmers had or give advice to newbies just starting out.

Once parked, Lucy grabbed the burlap sack out of the back and headed into the store. Inside was crowded, and she had some trouble getting around farmers who had brought in their wheelbarrows. They were blocking aisles as they busily loaded them up with twenty-five- and fifty-pound bags of seed, fertilizer, and farming tools. Any other day, this would not have bothered her, but today, she was impatient and anxious to get what she needed and get going.

After going down a couple of aisles and having no luck getting by, she was finally able to inch around a farmer who hadn't started loading up his wheelbarrow and was able to tip it up so Lucy could squeeze past. She then made her way to the back of the store where she thought she might find what she was looking for. Searching frantically, she finally located the item, and wouldn't you know that it was up on the top shelf and out of reach. Completely frustrated that everything was slowing her down, Lucy stomped her foot and swore under her breath. Why in heck was it all the way up on the top shelf? Looking around to see if there was anyone who could help her, she opened her mouth to yell for help but stopped short, remembering that Negroes need to stay in their place and not start demanding that white folks hurry up and wait on them. Yelling could get her in big trouble plus draw attention to herself, which was the last thing she wanted to do.

Calming herself down, she began walking around, trying to find someone to help her. She was wandering near the back door when it suddenly opened and in walked Sonny, old man Terkel's son. "Sir, can you get that big red box off the top shelf over here for me?" Lucy asked while walking and pointing to where the box was sitting. "If I can ask, how come y'all keep it way up there?"

Sonny, grabbing the little ladder from behind one of the other shelves, mumbled, "Because this one here is the strong kind that the farmers use, and we don't want folks to get it mixed up with the one they use around their houses. With it being up here, I have to grab it for them and can always check to make sure they know this one you can't use inside the house."

While Sonny Terkel was getting the item down for her, Lucy realized she needed to buy something else so it would not be so obvious that she had only come in for this one item. She really didn't need the twenty-five-pound bag of fertilizer right now, but she could have Sonny get that for her as well. It also gave her a chance to make small talk with Sonny and explain how she was going to use her purchased item on the farm. Matter of fact, she could always give the fertilizer to Lou, not that he was around his farm that much to use it. More and more, he seemed to always be gone playing that guitar of his. He should count himself lucky to have that passel of kids since most of the farming tasks fell on them and that wife of his when she wasn't laid up having babies. Making her way to Terkel's cash register line, she noticed it was doing what it always did, move "slower than molasses in the wintertime." She should have expected it, though, for every time she had come in for seed, fertilizer, or the likes, it took forever. Old man Terkel wouldn't let anybody else run the cash register. It was his time to be friendly and helpful, and he loved doing just that.

Placing the sack and the fertilizer in the back of the pickup, Lucy got in and hesitated for a few minutes before pulling away from Terkel's and heading south toward Morgan Grocery Store. Even though Morgan's was located in the south-end section of Little Rock, which meant going about ten minutes out of the way, it was well worth the drive across the Arkansas River.

She had found the little neighborhood grocery store when she was in the process of moving to Scott, Arkansas, six months ago, following behind Lou. Lord, that man had turned her world upside down from the minute she had laid eyes on him and heard him make that guitar "fair-dee-sing." She remembered it like it was yesterday. Her girlfriend, Mary Ellen, had heard there was going to be a man playing at Rodell's Juke Joint up in Eudora, Arkansas. Folk around Lake

Providence, Louisiana, said that he was better than anybody they had ever heard, and that every time he came through and played there, he would have the place jumpin' 'til wee hours in the morning. So, she and Mary Ellen had decided to make the drive up 'cross the Louisiana border to Eudora. Lucy figured her old red "Tomcat," as she called her pickup, could make the drive from Lake Providence in about an hour or so if the fog coming off the ole Mississippi didn't set in.

It had taken longer getting to Eudora than Lucy had planned since she had made two wrong turns. Rodell's was just on the other side of Eudora and sat back off the beaten path in a wooded area known as Catfish Bog, so it was hard to find for someone who wasn't from around that neck o' the woods. When they finally pulled up to the juke joint, cars were everywhere, and it took a bit of time to find a parking space. Folks were in line and waiting to pay their twenty-five cents for admission, while others were milling about and standing around their cars. Since the windows were thrown open to get the breeze going through the place, one could easily see that the place was already more than half full. The recorded music floating through the open windows created a festive mood as people swayed and sang along. From the looks of things, some people would be content to enjoy the evening outside rather than pay the twenty-five cents admission and fight the crowd and the indoor heat.

Lucy decided immediately that she had not driven that far to stand outside or even be forced to stand in the back. She quickly figured out a way to get right up front and as close to the guitar player as she could. Once they got up to where the line had formed, Lucy took Mary Ellen by the hand, and saying, "Excuse us, please excuse us," she gradually pushed her way to the front. She did this while telling others in line that the guitar player was her brother. Darn, she hadn't even thought to ask Mary Ellen what his name was, but she'd deal with that problem if and when it came down to that.

When they reached the front of the line, Lucy flashed her big ole smile, leaned forward revealing a bit of cleavage, told the guy collecting the admission fee that she was the sister of the guitar player, and that he was supposed to have told them she and her friend were coming. At first, the door keeper looked a bit puzzled, but then after looking at Lucy's big brown eyes and flashing smile, he figured he may have been told and had just forgotten, or even if he hadn't, what the heck! He immediately beckoned for a waitress, leaned over, and whispered something in her ear. The next thing Lucy knew, she and Mary Ellen were sitting at a little table right in front of the place where the guitar man would be playing. *Whew*, Lucy thought, then winked at Mary Ellen as she realized that her little lie had just paid off big time. Now, she would have to clear the next hurdle and pretend that she was his sister once he came out. How in the world was she gonna pull that off? Oh well, she'd figure that out, too, by the time he entered the room.

Twenty minutes later after Lucy and Mary Ellen had ordered hamburgers, french fries, and soda pops, Mr. Guitar Man himself walked in through the back door. The crowd went wild! Lucy could only stare with her mouth open, for she had not expected to see what she was seeing. He was around five-feet-ten inches and nice looking, but it was the eyes and the slightly lopsided smile that took her breath away. Her heart began pounding in her chest so loudly that she felt everyone in the room could hear it. He took his time, enjoying the hoots, hollers, and whistles from the crowd before finally taking his seat. Once seated and ready to play, he looked up into the smiling face and mesmerizing eyes of Lucy and was transfixed. Realizing that she had to pretend to know him since after all he was her "brother," she waved and blew a kiss his way. He tipped his hat in response, and their eyes locked.

For the next hour, he played and sang, and Lucy knew he was singing only to her. During his first break as he was approaching their table, Lucy jumped up to give him a hug while whispering that she had told the guy at the door that she was his sister. He chuckled, returned the hug, and offered to buy her and her girlfriend a drink to celebrate the success of her deception. They talked his entire break. Between other sets, he and Lucy only had eyes for each other and acted as though they were the only two people in the world. She could have cared less about the wedding band on the ring finger of his left hand. Five hours later, Lucy knew her life had changed forever, that she would do anything to have him, and that she would follow him to the ends of the earth.

Two months after that fateful meeting, Lucy had picked up lock, stock, and barrel and moved up to Scott, Arkansas. It had been just her and her mother. She hated uprooting her mother from Lake Providence, where she had lived all her life and where she still had a few friends, but Lucy had been wanting to leave for some time. Before meeting Lou, she had entertained the thought of heading up north somewhere since lots of people from around those parts were heading that way looking for work and better opportunities. She felt she could work in one of the factories or even do hair since city folk always wanted to be looking good and getting their hair done. She had heard that one could make a decent living doing hair. Now after meeting Lou, she had found her reason to leave, and she was taking it. Whatever she had to do to get him and keep him, she was ready to do it.

Lucy had found out about Morgan Grocery the day she moved to Scott from Lake Providence. Miss Alberta, a friend of Lucy's mother who lived three doors down from where they lived, was the first cousin of the owner of Morgan Grocery. When Miss Alberta learned that Lucy and her mother were moving to Scott, she had asked if they wouldn't mind driving through Little Rock, which was about fifteen miles from Scott. She wanted them to take her cousin, Greg Morgan, some jars of her homemade barbecue sauce. That way, she wouldn't have to ship it to him. Apparently, he not only ran the grocery store but also sold barbecue sandwiches and slabs of cooked ribs on weekends. It was Miss Alberta's special sauce that helped Morgan's ribs become so popular. Lucy had made the delivery, tasted the ribs, and found what she liked to call "The best little grocery store and rib place in Arkansas."

Now, she was headed there to gather the remaining items on her shopping list. She knew they would have the fresh collard greens and salt pork to cook with them, and getting a hunk from that big ole block of yellow cheddar for the macaroni would make it too tempting to resist. Supper would be a grand meal that night! In fact, it would probably be better than the meal prisoners get right before they are executed.

Lucy could already see the huge jar of pickled pig's feet that sat right by the grocery store's door with the bell that always jingled when someone entered the store. The big jars of pig's feet and dill pickles that sat on top of the candy counter brought in almost as many customers as the meat, fruits, and vegetables. Kids especially liked the pickles with a big round stick of peppermint candy stuck right in the middle. In fact, the kids and their parents bought so many that it was hard to keep the pickles in stock. The pig's feet were almost as popular. Lucy's mouth started watering as she could almost taste the pig's feet. She would definitely take time to sit out under that big maple shade tree on the side of Lou's house, spread out a quilt, and slowly enjoy the pig's feet along with a bottle of orange soda pop after she had set everything in motion.

Once she was back in the car and heading toward Scott, she could not keep the grin off her face as she played the scene over and over in her head. After her plan had accomplished what she was hoping it would, there would be millions of chances for her to enjoy herself the way she had been dreaming about for months now.

"I can hardly wait!" she screeched, pounding the steering wheel with the sweaty palm of her left hand as a shiver ran down her spine.

FOUR

Ultimate Betrayal

JULY 11, 1941–EARLY MORNING

Neiomi struggled to open her eyes to respond to the crying of her newborn baby girl. She was already exhausted, and it had barely been twenty-four hours since she had given birth. Sitting up and pulling the pillow up and propping it behind her, she reached over, grabbed the baby, and placed her so she could gently put her left nipple in the baby's mouth. "There, there," Neiomi said, "is that what you crying for?" The baby sucked greedily on the nipple. Neiomi, again unable to believe that God had blessed them with another beautiful and healthy girl, could only stare and shake her head.

Using her little finger, Neiomi gently pried open the baby's clenched fist on her left hand as she again counted fingers and toes just to make sure they were all there. She had to chuckle because she had done the very same thing with her first born, then the next, and the next. Now here she was repeating it with her seventh child. Already, she could feel that there was something unusual or different about this baby, but she couldn't put her finger on why she was feeling this way. One thing she did know: this baby was a real blessing and had arrived just when she needed something to lift her spirit.

No one could have been more shocked than her when she found out she was pregnant. Lately, Lou had been traveling so much playing his guitar that he was seldom home, and when he was, there seemed to have been very few times they made love. She knew the guitar playing was the only thing keeping money coming into the house. The past seven years had been much harder than either of them could have imagined. The first year was horrible.

They had managed to get a crop planted, but it was small, and they had lost some to something they called boll weevil. Those little bugs ate up and ruined about half their crop. When they took what was left to market, then paid Mr. Johnston what they owed him for his share plus the rent for the mule, seed, and other stuff, they still owed lots of money at the commissary. Each year, it just got worse and worse, so Lou had to go back to doing more and more playing, which meant he was gone just about all the time. Most of the work fell on her and the kids. She was so thankful that her brother Lowell had let his son Clinton come over twice a week and help with the farm work, else she couldn't have done it. Even with his help, it was still hard, especially when she was pregnant. She was so lonely most of the time but tried not to complain because Lou was doing the best he could to try and take care of them.

She was grateful Lou had not been traveling and was there for the baby's birth. It had been an easy delivery compared to some of her others, and best of all, the baby was born healthy. Neiomi would be up and back to working in the fields in a few days, so she wanted to enjoy this little bit of time with her new little girl. Even though they now had one more mouth to feed, Neiomi knew this baby would be well taken care of just like her other children. She would make sure of that.

In spite of the struggle, there was always food on the table, thanks in part to her vegetable garden out back and some chickens they'd managed to get from one of the other share-cropper families. That meant fresh eggs every day and some fried or baked chicken on special occasions. "Right now," she thought, "I'm not going to worry about anything. I'm going to enjoy my new daughter that the good Lord just blessed me with. We've still got to name her, and I'm thinking about naming her after my aunt Beatrice. I don't think Lou would mind. Matter 'o fact, that's exactly what I'm going to name her, except it's going to be spelled Beetrice. This baby is bringing some sweetness back into my life, and just like the bees make honey to sweeten up stuff, that's what Little Bee is doing for us. "Yes, siree," Neiomi said aloud as she looked down at the nursing baby, "your name is going to be Beetrice, and I'm going to call you Little Bee for short."

Later the same day around noontime ...

Driving back to the plantation after finishing her shopping at Morgan Grocery, Lucy was so focused on the task at hand that she didn't bother responding to all the black and white striped chain-gang guys waving and grinning at her. She could have cared less. Lou was the only man she could think about, and it had been that way since she moved from Louisiana to this god-forsaken hell hole known as Scott. In fact, he was the only reason she had packed up and moved here six months ago.

No one would ever suspect that she was about to pull out all stops to get what she wanted, especially Neiomi. With a smirk, Lucy began speaking aloud to herself, "All them nosey plantation folk, the busy-bodies, the know-it-alls have no idea what I'm up to. It's fair payback for them sticking their noses into my business and doing all that talking behind my back. They've even gone to Neiomi with their gossipy lips and big-hipped meddling visits, but thank goodness she's too stupid and ignorant to listen and believe what they're telling her. Can't she see he don't love her? He's never home, because when he's not traveling, he's with me. So now, it's time for me to get busy. Their nosey plantation heads are gonna be turned, looking down the road to the east, and I'm gonna sneak up on them and 'strike' from the west. When the know-it-alls finally 'wake up,' it's gonna be way too late. Serves them right!"

Once Lucy passed the old grain mill which came up just before the turn-off to Johnston Plantation, she began to have a tad bit of doubt, so she began talking to herself again. "It really isn't my fault, and no one can blame me for what I'm gonna do. I am only giving in to the stirrings in my heart and the longing I feel when I'm away from him. Oh, the passion that man stirs in my loins when I am with him makes it hard to breathe, and I feel like I can't live without him. It's not wrong to crave something that's not mine and can't be mine unless I make it possible for him to be mine. I've got to have that man! And I'm ready to do whatever it takes to get him!"

Turning off the main highway and onto the dusty, rutted road that ran in between rows of cotton on the right and five-foot-high rows of corn on the left, Lucy's confidence had returned. "Full speed ahead!" she shouted. She felt her guts would shake out as her old Chevy hit one rut after another. Finally, she reached the old, dilapidated row house Lou called home. What a sorry state that house was in. In fact, the whole plantation looked like a dump heap.

Lucy brought the old truck to a halt, grabbed the burlap sack and the groceries, but left the fertilizer so Lou could get it later. She climbed the three rickety stairs to the porch, carefully avoiding the gaping hole left by two missing planks that had splintered off last summer, which Lou had never bothered to replace. At midday, the heat was suffocating, and flies were working overtime, buzzing and lighting everywhere they could. The heat was giving Lucy the perfect reason to offer Neiomi a nice cold bottle of Barq's orange soda pop, except it would be Lucy's special recipe and would help launch her plan. One knock on the screenless screen door brought a couple of Lou's screaming brats excitedly running to open it so that Satan herself could enter.

Lucy handed the food from Morgan's to the kids to carry into the kitchen at the back of the house. As much as she hated to do it, Lucy put on her biggest smile as she entered the middle room, Neiomi's bedroom. "Hello, Neiomi, how you and that brand new baby of yours doing today?"

Neiomi was pleasantly surprised to see Lucy yet grateful for the company. Propping herself up on one elbow, she answered, "Oh, Lucy, what a surprise! Little Bee and I are doing just fine, excepting for this heat and these flies that won't leave us alone. Here, come see my new beautiful baby girl."

Lucy hesitantly moved closer to the bed, took a quick look at the baby, then said as she hurriedly turned away, "Neiomi, I brought you some cold soda pop, you know with the heat and all. Let me go get it for you. Also, I plan to stay and cook dinner for you and the kids since you laid up with the baby."

Lucy's words brought a big dimpled smile to Neiomi's face. She welcomed her friend Lucy and the treat of an ice cold Barq's. As was custom in the Deep South, and especially on the Johnston Sharecroppers' Plantation, neighbors always came to help whenever someone was sick, had just had a baby, or had suffered a death in the family. She was thankful for Lucy who was being so thoughtful and had even offered to stay and prepare dinner that evening for the entire family. Perhaps Lucy was doing this as a way of thanking Neiomi for the time when she had been there for her.

After Lucy's mother suffered a stroke three months back, pregnant Neiomi had walked the mile from her house to Lucy's across Highway 165. Before Lucy's mother passed away, she had done it a couple of times, bringing fresh vegetables from her garden. Lucy was not very well-liked on the plantation, so most folk simply ignored her. Only Neiomi and a couple of other people attended her mother's funeral. Women on the plantation constantly warned Neiomi that Lucy could not be trusted and that she was a home-wrecker, but Neiomi paid no attention to the local plantation gossip. She'd always felt that everyone needed a chance, especially when they were going through difficult times, and Lucy was no exception. So, she ignored the gossip and offered a helping hand and a listening ear. That was the least she could do.

Now, Neiomi was reaping the benefits of being a thoughtful neighbor, and it felt good. She had barely finished enjoying the Barq's orange soda pop when her newborn began to cry, demanding to be fed again. *For goodness sake*, she thought as she smiled, *this has to be the hungriest little girl in the world right now*. She had almost forgotten how demanding newborns could be. It had been a couple of years since their last baby, Ruthie, had been born, yet she was certain that she did not want to eat constantly the way this baby did.

Speaking of babies, again, she could not believe she had gotten pregnant since Lou was seldom home. In fact, he was gone so much that folk on the plantation had even begun to call him the "Arkansas guitar traveling man." Yes, her life was a lonely one, but lonely or not, she loved him with all her heart and tried to be as understanding as a wife could be. She hoped that this fall would bring about a hefty harvest and provide enough money to pay off their debt at the plantation commissary. Every year, that bill just seemed to get higher and higher, and there was always a balance carried over onto next year's bill. Hopefully this year, there would also be enough left to last until the following harvest. That way, Lou wouldn't have to work so hard and spend so much time away from the family.

Smiling, she gently lifted Little Bee and held her to her right breast, content to let her nurse until she was full. An indescribable warmth spread throughout Neiomi's body as she held her baby close. She then looked at the baby from one side, then the other, trying to decide whether she favored her or Lou the most. *Of course, she looks like me because Lou's never been that beautiful*, she thought as she snickered to herself. *Matter of fact, I'm not that pretty, either, but as far as looks go, Little Bee's got a better chance of looking like me than she's got looking like Lou.* She snickered again, then became serious as she marveled at the awesomeness of God's newest creation, this brand new human being.

For some reason, at that very moment, a shiver went through Neiomi's body which frightened her a bit, but she quickly shook it off. *Why would I be shivering in this heat?* she thought. Gently caressing the baby's body, Neiomi felt a mother's love so strong that she thought her chest would burst. She knew that as long as she breathed, she would do whatever it took to keep this baby safe and protected. Neiomi felt deep down in her soul that Little Bee was special, that she was blessed, and would experience many miracles throughout her life. Yes, it was a great time to be alive and to have a new baby again.

About a half-hour after enjoying the soda, Neiomi started to feel a little queasy and noticed a couple of black spots forming on her arm that looked like bruises. She didn't give it much thought and was preoccupied with taking care of Little Bee who seemed to be whimpering and whining more than crying. This seemed odd, for she usually quieted down and fell asleep right after her feeding. Neiomi tried to hold, rock, and sooth her, but Little Bee continued to squirm and fidget. Neiomi blamed it on the intense heat. It had to be a sweltering ninety-plus degrees, and no air was stirring or coming through the side window. She called her oldest son, Arthur, to bring a piece of paper in so she could fan herself and Little Bee and shoo away the flies that had become a nuisance. Fanning the paper wasn't much help with the heat, but at least it kept the flies from attacking her and the baby.

It was a little after six that evening. Neiomi had just enjoyed a delicious meal of fried chicken, collard greens, mashed potatoes and gravy, and macaroni and cheese. She had fussed a bit at Lucy about giving her such hearty helpings of food, but Lucy just shrugged it off and said she was trying to help Neiomi regain her strength and get back on her feet faster. Lucy had even come in a couple of times to refill her glass with lemonade she had made in the S...OS water jug with the fading letters. Neiomi got a second shiver when she noticed the water jug and also noticed that each time Lucy poured the lemonade, her right hand trembled so badly that she had to steady the jug with her left hand.

Neiomi chided herself as being foolish and completely out of her mind to even think that she was in some kind of distress, yet she still couldn't shake the uneasy feeling. She had promised herself she wouldn't eat too much, but the fried chicken along with the mac and cheese had smelled so good that she had managed to eat everything on her plate in spite of a queasy stomach. The potatoes and gravy had tasted different from what she had been used to, but she chalked it up to her overly sensitive sense of smell and taste that had started to change during her second month of pregnancy. She had no idea why that problem was still hanging around. Not wanting to hurt Lucy's feelings, she had managed to force herself to swallow the last of the gravy-saturated mashed potatoes. Now, she was regretting that she had eaten so much.

After dinner, Neiomi knew she had to get Little Bee fed before she could take a nap and before that little girl's two-hour alarm went off again. That baby had such a strong cry that she could wake up the dead. Perhaps she was going to earn a living being a human alarm clock when she grew up. The demands of the every-two-hours feedings took a toll when you had a newborn in the house, and boy it was already starting to wear Neiomi out. She was looking forward to getting some much needed sleep.

Little Bee, who still seemed fussy and restless, had only been nursing about ten minutes, when all of a sudden, Neiomi began feeling dizzy and nauseated at the same time. As she started to lean over to grab a rag lying on the bed to put it to her mouth, so much blood squirted from her nose that it went everywhere, staining the sheet, her gown, and Little Bee's body. Trying to get the blood off the baby, Neiomi began to panic, for she had never experienced anything like this with her other six children. Telling herself to calm down, she tried to slow her breathing but noticed she was panting like she had run a mile down the road. Seeing more bruises appearing on her hands and arms didn't help either.

Fighting the panic that was rising in her throat and sending her heart rate through the roof, she knew she could no longer hold the baby. "Alma ... A-l-m-a, come here and hold Little Bee for a minute," she called as she tried to keep her voice from shaking. Even though getting out of bed was still a little awkward and painful, she felt she had to get to the outhouse as quickly as possible. The problem was, the outhouse was located some twenty feet back from the house. Calling Lou to help her as she scooted to the edge of the bed, she then noticed that blood was coming from the lower part of her body and had soaked through to the mattress. At that moment, a pain shot through her head that left her feeling like someone had just smacked her upside the head with a baseball bat. "Lou," she called in a panicked voice, "Lou, get in here right now! Help me ... help ..." The blood was now pouring from her nose like a faucet that would not turn off. At the same time, she felt something warm running out of her left ear. Was that blood too?

"Oh! My! Lord!" she screamed. "I'm bleeding, I'm bleeding ... like the rats do!" What had Lucy put in her food? Had she been poisoned? Everyone on the plantation knew that rat poison made the rats bleed out, and that was just what she was doing now ... bleeding out. That was why the potatoes and gravy had tasted so strange ... and the lemonade ... and, oh my Lord, the S...OS on the jug had been a warning she had ignored. Realizing now that she had been poisoned by the same woman who everyone said was sleeping with her husband hit Neiomi like a ton of bricks falling on her head. How could she have been so stupid and not believed what they had been trying to tell her? She fought to suppress a scream, fighting both the physical and emotional pain she was experiencing, not knowing which hurt the most. She! Had! Been! Betrayed! "Where is Lou?" she mumbled weakly to no one in particular, for the heat and what the poison was doing to her body was making it hard to breathe. *Why is it taking so long for him to get in here?* she thought.

Sharp pains were coming so strongly and rapidly now that she couldn't think, and they were far worse than any she had ever experienced, even worse than the pain she had gone through yesterday during childbirth. She tried to call out again but winced as another sharp pain doubled her over. Meanwhile, Alma had gone outside to get her dad but learned he had gone down the road to visit a neighbor. Just as she was coming back into the house and shaking Little Bee trying to get her to stop crying, she noticed there was bloody spit-up all around the baby's mouth. Panicking, she ran into the room to tell her mother but stopped short and screamed as she rounded the corner of the bed. Both Neiomi and the bed were covered in blood. At that very moment, Neiomi let out a blood-curdling scream that could be heard a mile away.

Then, everything started to blur as Neiomi fell back on the bed, writhing in excruciating pain. Fighting against a shaking that seemed to be taking over her body and the fogginess clouding her brain, she called out to Alma again when she heard Little Bee squirming and crying. Rushing to get back over to the bed, Alma said, "Momma, Little Bee's spitting up a whole lot of blood, and I can't stop her from crying! Momma!" Alma screamed, "You and Little Bee both bleeding!" Running over to the window, she yelled to her brother Arthur, "Run as fast as you can and go get Daddy and tell him that Momma's got blood everywhere, and Little Bee's bleeding too!"

Meanwhile, Neiomi was struggling to deal with the pain and, at the same time, trying to stay focused. She wanted to ask Lou why he had let his woman come into their house and poison her, but she couldn't manage to get the words out because of the pain and her going in and out of consciousness. Through her fogginess, though, she realized that her baby had also been poisoned. Her body began shaking violently and uncontrollably, and there was no end to the blood that was now exiting every orifice of her body. Another blood-curdling scream came from somewhere so deep in her body that it sounded like it came from the pit of hell. Anyone walking down the dirt road that ran a quarter of a mile from their house would have been able to experience the outcry of her suffering. There would be many more … eventually tapering off to whimpers as she struggled to catch every breath. Fighting suffocation, hemorrhaging, and unbearable pain, Neiomi began praying for death, pleading to die, and finally, God had mercy on her and granted her peace. With her dying breath she mumbled, "Oh Lord, save my baby, my ba—"

FIVE

Saying Farewell

The incessant ringing of the phone at a quarter to midnight jolted Sophie out of a deep sleep. "Who on earth is callin' this time o' night?" she mumbled. Dragging herself out of bed, she made her way to the little table in the hallway that held the dial-up telephone. Leaning forward and fumbling to find the phone in the dark, she was able to grab up the receiver just before the sixth and final ring. "Hello, hello," she said anxiously into the mouthpiece, clearing her throat to remove the phlegm that always collected while she was sleeping. The connection had a lot of static, and she had trouble hearing the voice on the other end. "Can you speak up because I can barely hear you?"

"Aunt Sophie, this is your niece Annette, your brother Isom's oldest daughter. I live in Scott near Cousin Lou. I'm sorry to be calling so late, but he wanted me to call and tell you that his wife, Neiomi, died, and they're having the funeral tomorrow at eleven. He wants you to come down since his mother won't be able to make it all the way from Kansas City in time. You know with this heat and all, they need to get her buried as soon as possible. Do you think you can come?"

Sophie, now sitting down on the bench beside the phone and shaking her head in disbelief, finally stuttered, "Wa-wa-wait, what did you say? Did you say that Lou's wife died? You mean, sh-she's dead?"

"Yes, ma'am. She died a couple of hours ago," Annette replied.

Sophie, looking stunned and shaking her head vehemently as though trying to clear the fog from her sleepy brain, continued to murmur, "But that can't be? Neiomi's a young woman and looks real healthy and strong every time I see her. Pretty woman too. Did she get sick suddenly?"

"Auntie, she got real low sick all of a sudden after she had the baby yesterday morning. It may have had something to do with the baby, but I don't know. Some folk are even saying she might have been poisoned, but I'm not sure about that either. You know how folks start talking and making up stuff, and gossip is real bad down on the plantation where Lou lives. Anyways, I gotta go because I need to make a couple more calls, but I sure hope you can make it to the funeral. I'll let Lou know I got in touch with you. Please try to come, okay, Auntie? Bye-bye now."

Sophie sat there in the dark on the bench next to the phone table for what seemed like an eternity before she finally managed to rise. Lacking the strength to pick up her feet, she simply shuffled them across the hardwood floor back to the bed. She flopped down with such force that the bed bounced hard, causing her husband Blake to bolt upright. "What the heck is going on?" he asked while squinting and trying to see Sophie in the dark without his glasses.

My nephew Lou's wife died a few hours ago, and they want me to come down to the funeral tomorrow morning," she mumbled as though in a trance. "I just don't know how that woman could have up and died. I sure want to go to the funeral, but who can I get to take me?"

Blake, now fully awake, was sitting on the other side of the bed scratching his head. After a couple of minutes, he said, "Umh, umh, umh! Did they say how she died, like was she in an accident or something?"

"Naw, from what Annette said, she just got real sick, then up and died," Sophie responded. "I guess Neiomi had a baby yesterday morning, and that might have had something to do with it." Sophie thought about telling Blake about the poison thing Annette had mentioned but thought she'd best just keep her mouth closed and let it be for now. Besides, she wasn't real sure she heard it right, and maybe Annette had said something else.

Blake, still trying to come up with a way to get Sophie down to the funeral, finally offered, "Why don't I go across the street to Fred Wiggins' house come daylight and see if he can take you? Tomorrow is Saturday, so he might be able to do it. Had I known earlier, I could have done it, but I've already told them down at the railroad station that I'd work. Since I'm kind of new there, I don't want to mess up now. I know Fred works nights sometimes, even though he has his own shop down on 16th Street, but if he didn't work last night, he might not be too tired to drive you down there. Scott isn't that far, so it shouldn't take any longer than an hour or a little better, depending on traffic."

Sophie, traumatized by the news of Neiomi's death, sat transfixed for the next four or so hours, rocking back and forth and moaning, "Oh Lord, oh Lord, oh Lord. Ump, ump, ump. What is Lou and all them kids gonna do now?" She didn't realize she had dozed off until the sun, coming through their bedroom window, hit her in the face and woke her up with a start. She called out to Blake, waking him from a fitful sleep. He hurriedly got out of bed, grabbed his overalls from the back of the rocking chair, and put them on as quickly as he could. Grabbing his baggage porter's cap off the hall tree, he headed out to walk over to the Wiggins' house located about 100 feet diagonally across the street on the corner. After ringing the bell several times, Wyola Wiggins finally cracked the front door and peeked through the small opening, squinting to try and see who on earth would be calling at this time of morning. "Oh, good morning, Blake! What on earth brings you out so early?"

"Sorry to bother you this early, Miss Wyola," Blake said apologetically, "but is Brother Fred up yet?" You see, we have a death in the family, Sophie's nephew's wife, and I'm trying to get somebody to drive her down to Scott to the funeral this morning. She just found out about it late last night."

Wyola, now realizing the urgency of the situation, responded, "Blake, I am so sorry to hear that. Let me see if Fred is awake. Come in, come in! You don't have to stand out there on the porch."

Blake, following the customary Southern tradition when entering someone's house, removed his cap as he entered and stood just inside the door. He did not want to track dirt into their living room or sit on their furniture wearing the overalls he had done yard work in yesterday. The Wiggins had always had one of the nicest homes in the neighborhood, and Blake had always admired it. He remembered like it was yesterday when Fred had asked him to come over and help him put down their hardwood floors. Man, it was hot, and it must have been pretty close to ninety percent humidity. They had worked and worked on that job, had one heck of a time getting the boards to match up, and constantly worried about the moisture causing the boards to gap later on. But finally after about two weeks of working on and off, they had gotten all the flooring down. Then came the job of staining it.

Miss Wyola had bought this beige floral couch and matching chair with wooden trim from an antique store, and she wanted the floor stained to match the wood on them. They had looked and looked for that color and finally had to have the guy at the paint store mix up a couple of colors to get it to match. Even after he mixed it up, it took four coats of that stain before they finally got the floor color the way she wanted. Blake had to admit, though, that even after ten or so years, the floor was still holding up good, and the big round throw rug she had put in the center of the room made it look like a picture in one of those home magazines.

After several minutes, Fred Wiggins came slowly out of his bedroom, rubbing his eyes and trying to clean his glasses with the bottom of his shirt. "Morning, Blake. Wyola tells me Sophie's niece died down in Scott. She's trying to get down there to the funeral this morning?"

"That's right, Fred. Is there any way you could drive her

down? I'd be happy to pay you. I would drive her myself, but I just got this new job with the Rock Island Railroad, and they require me to work two Saturdays every month. I told them I would take the second and fourth Saturdays, which means I have to work today. Since it's only been a short time that I've been working there, I can't start taking off this soon."

Fred Wiggins thought for a few seconds, then shaking his head, said, "Blake, I really hate to tell you this, but my old Buick's been acting up lately, and to tell you the truth, I'm kinda scared to take it out on the road. I know Scott isn't that far, but in this heat, I'm afraid the thing might get out there on that highway, overheat, and the radiator starts boiling over. Is there anybody else you could get to drive Sophie down there?"

"Right now, Fred, I don't know of anybody else who isn't working since most of the other fellows do yard work for the white folks on Saturdays to earn extra money," Blake responded. "I'm sure praying I can find somebody. That boy needs his Auntie to be there, especially with his mother not being able to come from Kansas City on such short notice."

Blake hung his head, walked slowly back across the street, and gave Sophie the bad news. He tried making several more phone calls but had no luck finding anyone who would pick up the phone. Before leaving for work, he told her she probably wouldn't be able to make it down to the funeral since he couldn't find her a ride.

Three hours later while loading baggage onto a train bound for Chicago, Blake got the good news. Joe, one of the other baggage porters, came out to tell him that he had a message in the office. Making his way through the hot, stuffy, and crowded little waiting room designated for "Coloreds Only," he finally reached the tiny ticket window. Ticket Agent Johnson informed him that his wife and somebody named Fred were on their way to the funeral. No other details were available. Blake would later learn that Fred Wiggins had gotten his mechanic to patch up the radiator enough to make it to Scott and back. Blake walked from the waiting room, shaking his head and thinking, *Man, that Fred Wiggins sure came through for us when we really needed him. That's what I call a good man and a good friend, and he is a real blessing to us right now.*

The ride down to Scott seemed to take all day as Sophie fidgeted and twirled her thumbs around each other. As was proper when paying respects to the dead, she was wearing her Sunday best hat. She decided since it was so hot, she would wait to put her gloves on right before going into the church, so they were in her pocketbook. When they got into Scott, they stopped and asked a man walking along the highway how to get to the Johnston Plantation. He wasn't sure which one was the Johnston Plantation and ended up sending them to the Scott Plantation instead.

Once they realized that they were in the wrong place, they were told to go back and look for the old Watson Grain Mill and make a left just before it. Once they hit the dirt road on Johnston Plantation, they wandered down several badly rutted roads before finally reaching the little whitewashed clapboard church. It stood out because it was the only building on the plantation that was white, other than what looked like the owner's house, and not looking like it was falling apart. There was a little steeple and bell tower right over the front door of the church. As they pulled up, people were standing outside and on the steps so they knew the funeral service had already started and that the church was probably packed.

In spite of the heat, Sophie quickly put on her white gloves before Fred helped her out of the car. As they approached the church, one lady came over to inform them that there wasn't even standing room inside, and that the usher wasn't letting anyone else go in. Sophie responded, "Oh, honey, I'm Neiomi's auntie, and I've come from out of town, so I know they're gonna let me in. I hope they can find me and Mr. Fred here a seat. He's the one who drove me down here."

Immediately, the lady, feeling special because of her new position of escorting the out-of-town guests, took Sophie by the hand and led her toward the steps. "Make way for Neiomi's auntie. Please move so we can get Neiomi's auntie inside," she said as she led them through the little crowd gathered in front of the steps. Once they reached the door, the lady whispered to the usher that this was Neiomi's auntie, and she took over from there.

As expected, the place was packed and every window thrown open as wide as possible to take advantage of the little air that was stirring. There were also a couple of little fans sitting in the front of the church and turned toward Neiomi's family to try to make it a little cooler for them. With the usher leading the way, folks started moving aside to allow Sophie and Fred to make their way to the front. In spite of the pastor being in the middle of the eulogy, Lou, seeing his aunt Sophie, jumped up and came to meet her and to give her a tearful hug. Two of Lou's children got up from their seats to make room for Aunt Sophie and Fred and sat on the floor by their dad and Lou's twin sister, Lula.

Sophie and Fred had only been seated for a minute or so when she noticed the pastor kept repeating what sounded like a warning. "Mark, the seventh chapter and verses twenty through twenty-three says, 'What comes out of a person is what defiles them. For it is from within a person's heart that evil thoughts come—sexual immorality, murder, adultery, and the likes ... all these evils come from inside and defile a person.' There is so much evil in this world today, and some of you all sitting right here under the sound of my voice know just what I'm talking about. For in your heart is evil. The sin within you is causing you to do evil things. But beware, because God is still on the throne, and one day, you're going to be judged, and you're going to pay. Mark my word, reckoning day is a-coming."

Good Lord, thought Sophie, *I've been to many a funeral, but I've never heard that kind of eulogy, not nary a one like this before now. Something's just not right here. Now, what was it that Annette was trying to tell me last night about the gossip?*

During the final viewing following the eulogy, emotions ran rampant, and Sophie thought her heart would break when Neiomi's sister and two brothers went up to her casket. Her sister started crying uncontrollably, then collapsed. One of her brothers moved quickly to catch her to keep her from hitting the floor. He ended up carrying her out of the church.

The other brother started shaking his head and began screaming, "Somebody's gonna pay for this! Somebody's gonna pay for her murder! You hear me?" he yelled as he whirled around and stared directly at Lou.

Sophie turned toward Lou and noticed that he had leaned

over and was rocking back and forth on elbows that he had placed on his knees. His head was bowed, and he was dabbing his eyes with the handkerchief someone had handed him. Several family members got up and attempted to calm her brother Lowell down to keep his outbursts from completely disrupting the service. Sophie allowed her mind to wander back to what Annette had said about Neiomi ... and ... poison.

Had Annette actually said poison, or had she been half asleep, in total shock, or just imagined it? From the looks of things here, she had actually heard it. *Oh! My! Lord! Was that poor child actually murdered? Did somebody poison her? Who was it and why?* Sophie's mind was running amuck now. She felt a shiver and now better understood why the pastor had talked so much about evil during the eulogy.

Before she realized it, the funeral was over. As the family filed out behind Neiomi's casket and exited the church, the church bell began to toll. The outburst in the church had unnerved a lot of people, and no one uttered a word as they silently walked from the church to the cemetery located about a hundred or so feet behind the church. The bell continued to toll until all the mourners had reached the gravesite, and the pallbearers carrying Neiomi's pine-box casket had placed it on the boards laid across the open grave.

Sophie was offered one of the few chairs that had been placed beside the grave for the family. She took her seat and accepted the fan offered to her just as the graveside service began. Again, she was having trouble staying focused as she wrestled to come to terms with the possibility that Neiomi may have been murdered. *Who on earth would murder a woman with six children and a newborn? What did she do that was so bad that somebody would murder her?* she wondered.

Sophie had not been paying attention and did not notice the commotion between Neiomi's family and Lou taking place down at the other end of the grave. Ronnie, Neiomi's younger brother, had gotten up in Lou's face and was yelling, "Did you have something to do with Neiomi's poisoning? Huh? Huh? If you didn't, then you sure as hell know who did because it happened right in your house. Why won't you answer me?"

"Stop it!" Sophie screamed as she got up from her chair and started walking in their direction. "Oh, no! You're not gonna act like this here at your sister's gravesite. You all stop it! You stop it right this minute! How are you gonna stand up here and disrespect your sister's funeral by getting into an argument with her husband? Can you at least wait until they put her in the ground?" Reluctantly, but out of respect for Aunt Sophie, Ronnie turned around and walked to the other side of the grave, all the while glaring back at Lou who twitched nervously where he stood.

Following the pastor's "Ashes to ashes, dust to dust" closing of the graveside service, folks began to leave. Some began walking toward gravesites of departed loved ones or friends while others turned back toward the church and the dirt road that led back to their little shacks. Groups of mourners could be seen whispering and shaking their heads as they walked along.

For the next several weeks there would be non-stop gossiping and rehashing of everything that had happened regarding Neiomi Elaine Wilson. The mystery of her sudden death, the claim that she had been poisoned, the belief that

Lou's woman Lucy had done the poisoning, and her brothers' outbursts at the funeral and gravesite. All would be fodder for weeks of gossip. Plantation folk longed for any news or event that provided some distraction to an otherwise daily routine of hard work and boredom. A few folk, feeling sorry for Lou, started toward his house to sit a spell and try to console him and the kids. Others, including those who had tried to warn Neiomi, continued on past the house, heading in different directions.

Lou, who had lingered after the others left, now walked over and stood next to Neiomi's casket to take a final look before a couple of men would lower it into the grave and begin shoveling dirt over it. He was startled when her oldest brother, Lowell, walked up beside him. Lou looked up into cold steel gray eyes and heard a voice so low and menacing that it felt like the serrated edge of a dagger piercing his body. It sent chills through his entire being, body, and soul. "Rumor has it that your woman did this to my sister. Everybody on the plantation knows you two were having an affair. They say my sister suffered, hollered, and bled-out for at least a couple of hours, if not more. They say that you could hear her blood-curdling screams all the way across the plantation. Well, I'm here to tell you that somebody's gonna pay for her murder, and that's not a threat. That's a promise." Then, Lowell was gone.

Lou stood motionless for what seemed like an eternity. At that moment, he regretted every single minute he had been unfaithful to Neiomi. How on earth could he have treated her that way when all she had ever done was to love him in spite of his faults and work her fingers to the bone to help run the farm and make a comfortable home for him and the kids? The few mourners that were still hanging around made sure they steered clear and gave him space as he was saying his final goodbye to Neiomi. So much was running through his mind he was having trouble focusing, and Lowell's words kept ringing loudly in his ears.

After what seemed like an eternity, he felt he had to get going. So, willing his feet to move, Lou turned around and followed the others, stumbling several times as he made his way over a few graves. Once back in front of the church, he headed out to the dirt road leading to his house. The tears that he had tried to hold back since the whole horrible event started yesterday now came like a downpour. What on earth had he done?

His whole world was crumbling around him, and he had no idea how to deal with it. How had he managed to make such a mess of his family's life? Neiomi, the healthy baby she had given birth to just a couple of days ago now on the brink of dying, the children he would now have to raise alone … all because he couldn't keep his hands off of Lucy. Now, it had come down to this. For the first time since he could remember, he felt trapped and scared beyond belief.

SIX

The Aftermath

S ophie carefully climbed the rickety steps and opened the screen door with the missing screen. The smell was overwhelming as she entered the little dilapidated house, a carbon copy of most shotgun-type houses found on sharecropper plantations throughout Arkansas. The place reeked of old wood, soiled furniture, rotting food, and a smell she could not quite put her finger on, but one that over-powered all the rest. *Good Lord, the place is a mess!* she thought. *And it stinks to high heavens in here.* Even with the door open, breathing was almost impossible. The heat was suffocating, and flies had taken up permanent residence.

Five people were already gathering in the tiny front room, and there was nowhere to sit. Sophie could now see why some of the folk had stayed outdoors, lingering under the two shade trees on the side of the house. A couple of others, including Fred Wiggins, had found seats by sitting on the edge of the porch, taking advantage of the little shade provided by the roof but being careful to avoid the gaping hole left by the missing boards. All were trying to catch a little breeze and some relief, hoping to make the sweltering heat a little more tolerable.

Sophie was just about to enter the middle room to see if she could find a chair when the young lady sitting on the old caved-in threadbare settee got up and offered Sophie her spot. Sophie nodded and murmured, "Thank you, honey," knowing the young lady was showing respect for her elder. She had been hoping to find a chair rather than having to squeeze in between other sweaty bodies, but she just smiled and graciously accepted the seat. Once seated, however, she immediately became aware of the tension in the room, the undercurrent of mumblings about Neiomi's death, and the outbreak of threats that had taken place at the funeral and gravesite.

"You Lou's auntie?" said the toothless woman sitting next to her. Sophie nodded as the woman continued. "Lord, this sure is a mess what's going on with Neiomi's death and all."

Sophie, all of a sudden, felt her heart starting to pound, and there was a swelling in her throat, so much so that she felt like she would choke any minute. She could barely breathe enough to get out the words, "Do you know what happened to her?"

The toothless woman couldn't wait to begin sharing the gossip with Sophie. "They say she was poisoned by one of Lou's women, and that everybody knows it too. You know, he's been messing with that Lucy for a spell now, and I figure she just wanted Neiomi out of the way so she could move herself right on in here. It's a doggone shame, yes it is, because that woman had no business coming in here and killing Lou's wife."

At that very moment, Sophie thought she heard a cat meow and immediately jumped up from the settee, asking, "Wh-where's the cat?" as she looked around the room anxiously. The toothless lady opened her mouth to answer, but before she could, Sophie again heard what she thought was a cat meowing. "Oh Lord, I gotta get out of here because I'm allergic to cats, and I'll be sick as a dog if I get too close to them," Sophie said as she began moving toward the front door.

The tall lady who had been standing by the door leading into the middle room stopped Sophie and said, "Miss, that's no cat. That's Neiomi's sick baby. They say she real low sick, and she probably won't make it past tomorrow."

In all the confusion and outbursts at the services, Sophie had completely forgotten about the baby. "Oh my goodness, where's the baby now?"

"She's back there in the middle room," the lady mumbled while gesturing to the next room.

Without saying another word, Sophie hurriedly made her way to the doorway. As she pushed past the lady and entered, what she saw and smelled stopped her dead in her tracks. It took all she could do not to throw up as she looked over on the bed. The stench was so bad that she just knew the baby was already dead, because how could any living thing smell that rotten?

Then, it hit Sophie as she mumbled, "That's what I smelled when I came into the house!" She reached deep down into her soul and willed herself to move toward the bed, holding her nose with one hand and shooing the flies off the baby with the other. There, lying on the blood-soaked mattress was Neiomi's baby. "Lord, have mercy," she cried, almost too stunned to move. Then gathering her wits about her, she began screaming at the top of her lungs, "Somebody come here, come here! Come here right now!"

Several people scrambled to the doorway and looked in but stopped short of coming in because of the stench. Meanwhile, Sophie had waved her hands to shoo away the flies, then reached down on the bed to lift the baby into her arms, hoping she was not too far gone. The baby's little naked body was burning up and covered in dried blood, feces, and vomit. She had barely moved when Sophie picked her up. Tears welled in Sophie's eyes as she gasped and looked down on this dirty, smelly, blackened shell who had been a healthy newborn just a couple of days before. Speaking to no one in particular, she said insistently, "Why are you all letting this poor child lay here dirty like this? Anybody with a lick o' sense can see this child is sick and needs some help! You could at least clean her up. Where's Lou? Go get Lou right now!"

Lou had been lingering under a shade tree on the side of the house, talking to a couple of men friends who had stopped by. He was mainly trying to avoid stares and questions from nosey neighbors and recover from the chilling threat from Neiomi's brothers. Most of all, though, he was trying to avoid answering questions he knew Aunt Sophie was going to be throwing at him. Even though she was younger than his mother, nobody in the family wanted to mess with Aunt Sophie because she didn't play and would get you told off in a minute.

Lou looked around as Mc Kinley, his second oldest son, came running out of the house to tell him that Aunt Sophie was yelling for him to "Come here right now!" Lou knew that second, the tornado was about to hit, and all he wanted to do was make a beeline to the storm shelter out back, located a few yards behind the outhouse.

So much was going on in his mind right now that he couldn't think straight. He'd had no idea that his affair with Lucy would have resulted in Neiomi suffering the way she had. His ears were still ringing from listening to her agonizing high-pitched screams. In fact, every time he thought about it, it made the hair stand up on his back, and the lingering stench of death still permeated the house. Now on top of everything else, he was having to deal with a baby that was about dead. At least he didn't have to listen to the baby scream like Neiomi had because all she had done at first was whimper like a hurt dog, but now she wasn't even doing that. With notice-able reluctance, he excused himself to face what he didn't want to face: the unrelenting heat, the rotten smell, the accusing stares from folks sitting on the front porch and in the front room. As for the middle room, it had become hell on earth.

One look at his aunt Sophie's face as she stood there holding little Bee said it all. If looks could kill, he would be there in the cemetery with Neiomi right now. He expected a scream, but her barely audible voice held far more venom as she uttered, "How on earth could you let this happen to your baby? Don't you care? Huh? Do you even care if she lives or dies?"

Lou shifted from one foot to the other trying to come up with an answer that made sense as three of his children and a couple of neighbors, including the toothless woman, looked on. Stammering, he finally answered, "Auntie, I was trying to take care of Neiomi and the other kids, and I didn't really know what to do with a sick newborn baby. Alma here's been trying to look after her, but she won't eat. Just crying and whimpering and pooping and spitting up blood all the time." Raising his voice and showing his frustration, he continued, "I don't know what else you expect me to do!"

"Don't you raise your voice and get sassy with me because I'm about ready to knock you into the middle of next week, even if you are a grown man," Sophie responded, her voice trembling with anger. "This here is a crying shame!" she continued. "I gotta get this child out of here and to a doctor because she'll be out there in the cemetery with her mother if somebody don't do something. Do I have your permission to take her to Little Rock and get her some help?"

Lou, still reeling from everything that had happened during the past twenty-four hours, was not about to endure the tongue-lashing he was receiving from his own aunt Sophie in front of his neighbors without a fight. After what seemed like an eternity, he mumbled, "No, I don't want you to take her because I don't want the kids separated and—"

"What are you talking about, separated?" Sophie retorted angrily. "Do you see this child? Huh? Turn around and look at this child!" Sophie was screaming so loud now that folks who had been outside were now trying to peek into the room through the window. "I've never heard anything so stupid! Here, this child is near death, I'm trying to get her to a doctor, and you're talking about you don't want them separated. If this baby doesn't get some help, she's gonna be separated alright. She'll be separated from you all forever!"

Lou, struggling to salvage some semblance of his manhood, arrogantly responded, "She's probably gonna die anyway because she's got the poison thing like her momma, so I figure we should just let her be because there's not much we can do for her now."

After several minutes of arguing back and forth with Lou standing his ground about Aunt Sophie taking Little Bee, Fred Wiggins found his way to the middle room, and with a tone of urgency, said, "Sister Sophie, we've gotta go. I'm supposed to be at work by six-thirty this evening, and it's going on four o'clock now. Even though it's Saturday, we might run into traffic and people trying to make their way back into Little Rock, so we gotta leave right this minute."

Sophie turned to Lou, and asked in a pleading voice no one had heard since their conversation had started, "Lou, I'm begging you for God sake and for the sake of this child, please let me take her and save her life."

Lou, feeling this was the time to save face and show the onlookers he was still in charge, looked Aunt Sophie in the eye and gave her an emphatic "No!"

Given no other choice, Sophie, in spite of the dried blood and vomit, held Little Bee to her breast for what she knew would be the last time, then leaned over to place her gently back on the blood-stained bed. All of a sudden, Little Bee's body jerked as she grabbed the neck of Sophie's dress, opened her little eyes as wide as possible, and would not let go as she tried to place her back on the bed. *Where on earth did this puny, blackened skeleton of a baby find that kind of strength?* Sophie thought.

"Lord help me, but this baby's got more sense than all of

you put together," Sophie shouted in disbelief so loud that folks standing outside the window could hear. "She just gave me a sign and is telling me she wants to live! So help me, Lord, I'm gonna do everything in my power to help her live. Hand me that rag over there so I can wrap it around her. Lou, the only way this baby is not going out of here with me is you've gotta kill me, and if you don't kill me, she's going with me. You can call the law and have me arrested, but you can't do that before I get her to the hospital. Get out of my way!" Sophie yelled as she pushed past Lou and walked out of his house with Little Bee.

After Sophia and Fred Wiggins left, Lou stood in the middle of the yard. He watched the car as it kicked up dirt and hit rut after rut while making its way down the path leading from his yard to the main dirt road. He continued standing there staring long after the car had exited the plantation and turned left onto Arkansas State Highway 165, heading west toward Little Rock.

It was as if his whole world was falling apart right before him, and he had no control over anything anymore. As he turned and walked up the rickety steps, he knew his life was in shambles, just like the house.

SEVEN

Praying for a Miracle

University Hospital sat at the corner of 12th and Mc Almont streets on the east side of town in Little Rock. Sophie had only been there a couple of times in her life and had forgotten that the building took up an entire city block. Looking at this huge five-story building, she now wondered if she had made a mistake in coming here rather than going to the smaller one she knew more about, Arkansas Baptist Hospital over on 14th Street. She had heard somewhere that University Hospital was a good hospital and a place where they trained students to become doctors, so she figured they would have better doctors and better equipment here. *No,* she thought, *I gotta get this baby the best care they've got here in town.*

The ride back to Little Rock from Scott had been nerve-wracking as Sophie was still shaken from everything that had happened since they had left home this morning. There were the outbursts at the funeral and gravesite, the possibility that her nephew had killed or may have helped kill his wife, and now the pitiful condition of this baby who could die any minute. The least of her concerns up to this point was the argument she had had with Lou and the final decision she had made to take the baby without his permission. Turning to Fred Wiggins, she asked, "What I did back there, is that kidnapping?"

He nodded and answered, "Yes, Sister Sophie, and I believe we both could be in big trouble if your nephew decides to get the law involved."

"Oops! Oh well, if it was, then I can't think about that right now. I'll have to cross that bridge further down the road. I gotta think about getting this baby to a doctor now," she responded absentmindedly as she was bending over to try and see if Little Bee was still breathing. Even though she had always felt her faith in God was strong, doubt was trying its best to creep in now. Ignoring the uncertainty she was feeling, she bowed her head and silently prayed that they would make it to the hospital in time. She looked down at this tiny, blackened shell of a human being and thought, *Lord, how can any baby make it through what's happened to her? If there was enough poison in her mother's body to kill a full grown woman that fast, how on earth can a newborn live through that? Wonder why her skin is all black? What evil stuff went on in that house?*

A couple of times, it looked like Little Bee had stopped breathing, and Sophie had to lean over to put her face next to Bee's to see if she could feel her breath. She knew she ought to try and clean her up, but the baby's skin looked like it would tear if she tried to wipe it with the dry rag she had grabbed on the way out, and besides, she didn't have any water.

The drive back to Little Rock was taking f-o-r-e-v-e-r. She knew Fred was a good driver and a careful one, but for heaven's sake, the man was driving so slow she felt she could get out and walk faster. Sophie was about ready to tell him to move over and let her drive when she realized that he was being extra careful because he did not want to put more strain on the patched-up radiator. That could cause it to overheat and leave them stranded out here on the highway. She forced herself to keep quiet, sit back, and try to relax. She was finally able to breathe a sigh of relief when she saw the "Entering Little Rock City Limits, Population 88,039" sign. Hallelujah, they just might make it!

After pulling into the parking lot and finding a parking space, it took Sophie and Fred several minutes to find the hospital entrance designated for Negroes or "Coloreds," which was around the corner from the main entrance. The little cardboard sign was so faded that you could barely read the words, "Colored Entrance."

Once inside, the small waiting room was packed with wall-to-wall folks, and it was stiflingly hot and stuffy in spite of the small oscillating fan sitting on the counter in the corner. Midway the wall on the right was a small check-in window with a little door that was closed. The sign above the window read, "Wait here to check in." Several people were already waiting in line, and there was nowhere to sit. Panic started to set in again as Sophie realized that even though they had made it to the hospital, she could still end up losing Little Bee right here in the waiting room before she even got to see a doctor. From the looks of things, it was going to be a long, hot wait.

Unbeknownst to Sophie, Fred had gone over and softly spoken to the first lady standing in the check-in line. He briefly explained Sophie's situation and asked her if she would allow Sophie and the baby to cut in front of her when the window opened. The lady agreed after taking a look at Sophie and the baby. Fred then walked back over to where Sophie was standing and told her what the first lady in line had agreed to do. He explained that he had to leave immediately if he was going to make it all the way out to the south end to get home, change clothes, and drive all the way back downtown to get to work on time. He didn't want to risk losing his job where he repaired watches during the night at the MM Cohn Company. He promised her that once he got home, he would run across the street, briefly tell Blake what was going on, and have him come to the hospital.

Sophie, now realizing that she would be all alone for the first time since all of this started, felt tears welling up in her eyes. She thanked him for everything he had done and sadly watched as he walked out the door. At that point, she was feeling more alone than she could ever remember.

A few minutes after Fred Wiggins left, a large man who had been sitting in a corner chair watching Sophie struggling to hold the baby, and also noticing her swollen and deformed left foot, got up and offered his seat to her. She gladly thanked him and immediately took the offered chair. It wasn't until she looked up to watch him walk to the other side of the room that she noticed him limping, his right ankle swollen to twice the size it should have been, and the piece of gauze that was wrapped around it. She started to feel a little bit guilty, then realized she was exhausted, her feet hurt, and she needed that seat to try and make Little Bee as comfortable as possible. She wasn't used to holding a baby, either, and her arms were starting to ache.

She was glad there was a little space between her seat and where most of the other people were sitting since the odor coming from Little Bee's body was worse than day-old garbage that had been sitting out in the heat. She couldn't worry about that. By now, Little Bee's body was limp and burning up. Her eyes were closed and had been since that brief moment when Sophie had tried to lay her back down on the bed. There was no movement at all. Sophie knew that the fever had pushed her temperature through the roof and was trying to find something to fan the baby when she heard a stir.

Looking up, she saw people were moving toward the now-opened little door at the check-in window. The lady at the front of the line was frantically beckoning for her to hurry and get to the window. "Thank you, Lord!" she uttered as she hurriedly made her way there. Sophie was so nervous when the receptionist started asking her questions that she had trouble explaining why she was there, so she simply held the baby up for the check-in lady to see. The receptionist and everyone around her gasped, and the receptionist was so overcome by the sight of Little Bee's blackened and emaciated body that she immediately motioned for Sophie to come around the counter. Directly in front of her was a door that would allow her to enter so that the doctor could take a look at the baby.

Dr. Jimmy Higginbotham was a huge red-faced man who

wheezed when he walked, and the minute he walked into the little partition where Sophie was sitting, she wished even more now that she would have taken Little Bee to Baptist Hospital instead of bringing her here. Without acknowledging her or the baby, the first words out of his mouth were "whew, that baby stinks! Couldn't you at least have changed her diaper or given her a bath?"

Sophie was on the verge of tears as she tried to explain what had happed over the past six hours, how she had been in such a hurry to get Little Bee to a doctor to keep her from dying from the poison, and that she didn't have time to clean her up. "Doctor, can you please try to save her life, because if you don't, then she's gonna be dead and out in the cemetery with her momma," Sophie pleaded."

Doctor Higginbotham, placing his hand over his nose, came closer, pushed his glasses down on his nose, and peered over them to look down at Little Bee for a few seconds before mumbling something to himself. He then pushed his glasses back up on his nose, looked at Sophie, and said, "I hate to tell you this, but there's nothing we can do for this baby. You say her mother was poisoned and died yesterday?"

"Yes, sir, doctor!" Sophie answered. "They say the baby was nursing before her momma knew about the poison."

"Well that's too bad," Dr. Higginbotham continued, "because what her mother did was basically kill her own child. She should have known better than to nurse her baby if she was sick and knew something was wrong with her, even if she didn't know it was poison. There is no hope for this baby, and I'd venture to say she will be dead in three days if not sooner. My advice to you is to take her on home and try to make her as comfortable as possible. Sorry I could not be of more help to you and this baby."

"But doctor," Sophie said in a voice louder than what was considered appropriate for a Negro talking to a white person, "aren't you gonna examine her because she's real hot, and I think she's got a fever and all?"

"Woman, I don't need to examine her!" Dr. Higginbotham responded in a loud and chastising voice. "For I can see from here that the baby is almost dead. As I told you before, there isn't anything I can do for her, so you need to leave this room now and take her on home." With that said, the doctor left the little partitioned area and told the nurse to show Sophie and the baby the way back to the waiting room so they could leave the hospital.

As Sophie got up from the chair, her feet felt like the feet of a man working on the highway gang shackled with ball and chain. She could hardly drag them down the hall and back into the waiting room. All hope of saving Little Bee's life was gone. Sophie was asking herself, *How can I just go home and watch this baby die? First, her daddy just want to let her be and die. Now, this doctor wants me to just take her home so she can die. Lord, how am I gonna help this poor innocent child who's done nothing but just come into this world and be in the middle of the mess her daddy and his slut of a woman made?* There were no words to explain how she felt. It was like the doctor's words had hypnotized her, and she was in a trance.

She only came to her senses when she heard Blake's voice yelling, "Pet, Pet, I'm over here."

They rode home in silence, Blake knowing better than to

ask any question that would upset Sophie even more. He didn't let on about how shocked he was when he saw the baby. Good grief, what had been done to this child? The smell was overwhelming, but that was the least of his worries now. At least the wind blowing through the car from the opened windows helped with the smell. What they had to be concerned about now was doing everything humanly possible to save this baby.

During the ride from the hospital, Sophie was now realizing that Little Bee's only hope of living through this was in her hands. *What can I do?* she thought. "I know how to mix up some castor oil for colds and flu, and I know about taking a teaspoon of Black Draught for constipation, and I rub on some of ole man Watkins' Liniment for sore aching muscles, but none of them are any good for poisoning. Lord, help me to find a way to save this child from the poison," she moaned as she rocked back and forth in the front seat of the old black 1935 Ford. "Blake, this child is burning up with fever, and she's not even trying to cry anymore. She's as limp as an ole dish rag. I just don't know if she got enough fight left in her to make it."

As Sophie and Blake walked up the steps to the porch and she waited for him to unlock the front door, Sophie had made a crucial decision. Once the door was unlocked, she walked into the house, headed straight for the bedroom, and told Blake to stay out until she opened the door. She lay Little Bee on their bed, placed her right hand on the baby, and got on her knees.

Oh Lord, my God, in the name of Jesus!
I'm calling on you, so please hear my cry ... right now!
And pity my every groan.
Lord, have mercy on this child,
And send your healing virtue to flow from the top of
her head
To the bottom of her feet!
Lord ... have mercy on this poor little child,
Just as you had mercy on baby Moses when you saved
him from old, wicked Pharaoh!
And when Baby Jesus was born, you saved him from
the evil King Herod.
Lord, spare this child, for she has something to do in
this world for you,
Or else you wouldn't have let her be born.
The good book says, "Suffer the little children to come
unto Me,
And forbid them not, for such is the Kingdom of
Heaven!"
Lord, she's only a few days old, and the devil is trying
to take her out of this world.
But, today, I stand in the gap for her.
Satan, I rebuke you right now in the Name of Jesus!
Take your hands off her! She doesn't belong to you!
She belongs to the Lord!
Lord, you said that whatever we ask in your
Son's name
That you would grant it.
I ask for healing for this this child ... right now,
In the almighty name of Jesus.

Lord, raise her off her death bed
And purify her blood with the blood of Jesus.
I rebuke the death angel, in Jesus' name.
Work a miracle, Lord, so that the people will know it's
God working
And that you rule in the Kingdom of Man,
And beside you, there is no other!
With you, Lord, all things are possible to them that
Believe!
And, Lord, I sure do believe.
Satan, I command you to lose your hold and get your
hands off this child.
We're mourning the loss of this child's mother, Neiomi,
But I decree and declare that we are not gonna be
mourning the death of Little Bee!
Lord, increase my faith and give me the wisdom and
understanding on how to obey.
Lead me to know what I'm supposed to do.
I declare this day, "Little Bee, you're gonna live and
not die!"
Hallelujah! Thank you Jesus!
I pray this in the mighty name of Jesus.
Amen! A—men!

Sophie remained on her knees a few more minutes, then jumped up like a bolt of lightning had struck her. Hurrying and opening the door, she cried out, "Blake, the Lord just showed me that Miss Bertha across the street may be able to help because she's a mid-wife and kind of a doctor of sorts since she helps women birth babies. Go in there and watch the baby while I run over to her house and see if I can get her to come over and take a look at Little Bee.

A few minutes later, Sophie and Miss Bertha, a little out of breath, came hurrying into the house and made a beeline to the bedroom. Miss Bertha was still in her nightcap since she was usually getting ready for bed this time of the evening. She took one look at Little Bee and gasped, for even though she was used to seeing people sick and in bad shape, this was by far the worse she had ever witnessed. Finally, finding her voice after recovering from the initial shock, she was able to comment, "Oh my Lord, Sister Sophie, this child is in a bad way, and the doctor may be right about the three days because I don't know if we can save her."

Sophie, having found new strength and hope following her prayer, responded, "Oh yeah, she's gonna make it because God's gonna work a miracle here! He showed me during my prayer that she's gonna make it, and I believe that from the bottom of my heart. I just need you to tell me how to break this fever and how to get this poison out of her body."

Being encouraged by Sophie's faith, Miss Bertha now started putting on her "thinking cap," as she called it. "Well, I think if we can get the poison out of her, the fever will drop because the fever is nature's way of helping the body fight all that poison she's got in her." After a couple more minutes, Miss Bertha continued, "Sister Sophie, I kinda remember something my grandma once said when she was telling us about how one of her children, I think it was my uncle Robert, had gotten bit by a snake. It was a long time ago, but I think she said something about them using the sap from peach tree leaves to help draw out the poison. I don't know if it works or not, but it's not gonna hurt to give it a try. At least we're doing something, which is better than just doing nothing. Do you know anybody who's got a peach tree?"

Sophie could barely contain her excitement when she responded, "I got a great big ole peach tree right out there in my backyard. In fact, it's so big I've been telling Blake he needs to get out there and cut the branches back before they take over the whole backyard. What do you need me to do?"

Miss Bertha, still pondering her suggestion and hoping with all her heart that she had remembered it right, started telling Sophie, "What I figure is that we go out there and fill a great big ole bucket with leaves. Then, we're gonna bring them in the house, get a hammer, and start pounding them to get the juice out of the leaves. Once they're good and wet, we gonna put them on her little body. Do you have any kind of gauze that we could use to hold the leaves?"

"No, I don't have any gauze, but I do have the cotton flour sacks that we get when we go to the store and buy flour. I've got a whole stack of them all washed and clean," Sophie informed Miss Bertha.

"Oh, that's even better because all we have to do is put the leaves in the sack and pin the other end together to keep them from falling out. Let's get going!"

Within ten minutes, Sophie and Miss Bertha had the first sack all ready to go and placed it on Little Bee's naked body. All the while, they were both praying silently that the poultice would work. After about five or so minutes, Sophie started to notice the flour sack turning black. "Miss Bertha, look here!

Look at what's happening to the flour sack," Sophie said nervously.

"Oh, praise the Lord!" shouted Miss Bertha. "And thank you, Grandma, for that piece of advice. That's the poison being pulled out of her little body. Sister Sophie, let's double up and put one sack down and lay her on it, then put the other one on her front. That way, it's getting the poison out of her faster." This was the beginning of a ritual that would continue day and night for the next three days.

Meanwhile, Little Bee had started to squirm and tried to cry, but it was so weak that it sounded more like a kitten trying to meow while lying under a ton of blankets. Miss Bertha said, "I bet that baby is hungry as all get-up, and we need to get some milk into her little body."

Suddenly, they both realized that there were no baby bottles in the house, and by that time, all of the local stores were closed. "You know, Sister Sophie," Miss Bertha offered, "I think that Floyd's Drug Store down there on Ninth Street just might be open a little later than the other drug stores because of the ice cream parlor he's got in the drug store. Also, it's just one block from the Gem Theater, and ole Mr. Floyd usually keeps it open for folks looking for something to eat after the movie lets out. I hear that some nights, Floyd's is packed full of people way past 11:00, and since it's Saturday night, we just may be in luck."

Five minutes later, Blake was in the car and headed to the drug store to pick up baby bottles, cloth diapers, a tin of Carter's Black Drawing Salve to rub on Little Bee, and some tincture Miss Bertha said she needed. While Blake was running his errand, Miss Bertha had Sophie boil some cow's milk and add a little sugar so everything would be ready to go when Blake got back.

Once he returned, they filled a bottle and made several attempts to get Little Bee to suck on the nipple, but she was simply too weak. They even tried making a sugar-tit by putting a little bit of milk and sugar on the tip of a clean rag and putting it in her mouth but had no luck. After about fifteen minutes of trying, Miss Bertha came up with a different idea. "Sister Sophie, do you have a dropper, you know one like the one that comes with drops for your eyes?"

"Yes, I think there is one in the Dr. Watkins Menthol Drops bottle on the top shelf of the medicine cabinet in the bathroom. What are you gonna do with a dropper?"

"This baby is too weak to suck on anything, so we're gonna have to feed her by giving her little, tiny drops of milk from a dropper," answered Miss Bertha. "Let's get that dropper and boil it to get it sterilized and see if we can get some milk in her body." For the next several hours, the two women alternated between feeding Little Bee with the dropper and changing the flour sacks containing the peach leaves poultice. Finally, Miss Bertha ventured to say, "Sister Sophie, I think we're making some progress here, but this child has still got a long row to hoe if she's gonna make it. Right now, we've just got to keep on keepin' on."

One huge scare came during the afternoon of the second day. Miss Bertha had been sitting in the rocking chair next to the little wooden cradle Blake had managed to borrow from one of the neighbors, when she suddenly notice there was no movement of Little Bee's chest. Jumping up and gently picking her up, Miss Bertha lay the baby on the bed, held her mouth open, and began to blow into it while gently pressing on her chest. After three attempts, she heard Little Bee's faint cry. It was music to Miss Bertha's ears.

This scene would repeat itself a couple more times during that critical three-day period. Both women were praying Little Bee would pull through and prove Dr. Higginbotham wrong.

EIGHT

A Glimmer of Hope?

Wednesday was predicted to be a spectacularly beautiful day with cooler temperatures and less humidity. The weatherman had no way of knowing his prediction would be right on point, having nothing to do with the weather. Blake was the first to be up and about and noticed that Sophie had fallen asleep in the rocker next to the little wooden cradle. Tip-toeing softly around Sophie so as not to awaken her or Little Bee, he anxiously peeked into the cradle and got the surprise of his life. There looking up at him were two big eyes wide open. Even though the face was drawn, boney, and blackened, that was the most beautiful sight he had ever seen. "Pet, Pet, wake up!" he yelled. "The baby has her eyes open!"

"Huh? What?" she mumbled still half asleep.

"Pet, Little Bee has her eyes open," Blake shouted excitedly as he shook Sophie's arm to make sure she was awake.

"Hallelujah! Praise the Lord," she said as she peered down

into the cradle. Wanting to get a better view of this miraculous sign, Sophie jumped out of the rocker and joined Blake in peeking down into the cradle, smiling and hugging him from the side at the same time. "I think she's gonna make it, Blake, because that's the first time she's opened her eyes wide like that since the day I wouldn't leave her at Lou's. You've got to run over and get Miss Bertha so she can come and see this miracle. I know Little Bee is still weak and all, but this sure enough is a good sign."

While Blake made the short walk across the street to Miss Bertha's little shotgun house, Sophie could not believe how happy she was feeling and started singing with all the energy she could muster, "I thank you, Jesus, I thank you, Jesus, because you brought her from a might, a mighty long way. Oh … oh, I thank you, Jesus."

Sophie was so nervous she couldn't keep her hands from shaking but was hoping she could keep them still enough to pick up Little Bee. "Oh, I just knew you were gonna make it, baby," Sophie said aloud to Little Bee, hoping she would someday understand the miracle the Lord had just worked in her little body. As soon as Miss Bertha walked into the room, it almost sounded like an old-fashioned tent revival taking place as they started shouting—*thank you, thank you to the Good Lord*—hugging each other, jumping up and down, and crying tears of joy. Once the celebrating had quieted down a little, Sophie told Miss Bertha, "We've got to take her back to the hospital and show that Doctor Higginbottom he was wrong because she's made it pass the three days when he said she would be dead."

This time, she would make sure Little Bee was clean and

smelling much better. However when she started to wash her, it was much more difficult than she had thought it would be. Her body was so frail and her blackened skin almost as thin as tissue paper. Sophie feared hurting her or tearing the skin, so she sat her in a small wash basin and just drizzled water over her little body, trying as best she could to get some of the dried blood that had caked and still remained in places where the skin folded and creased. She then patted her dry with a soft cotton cloth.

Up to this point, Sophie had completely forgotten about clothes for Little Bee. Because of her condition and the fact that they were continually laying the flower sacks containing the poultice on her body, there had been no need for clothes. Today was different, though, because she certainly couldn't take her to the hospital in just a diaper. What was she going to do since Blake had already left for work? Again, Miss Bertha came to the rescue. One trip back across the street to Miss Sarah's house produced several little baby outfits that her three-year-old daughter, Betty Jean, had worn as a newborn. Little Bee was too tiny even for any of the newborn dresses, but at least she would be covered and going back to the hospital looking and smelling better than she had four days earlier.

It was mid-morning when they arrived at the hospital. Since Miss Bertha's daughter had agreed to drive Sophie and the baby there, Miss Bertha was able to come along. The morning shift was still on duty, so Sophie did not encounter any of the staff she had dealt with when she had brought Little Bee the past Saturday. The little waiting room was less crowded, so the three adults were able to find seats. After a twenty-minute wait, Sophie was escorted in to see Dr. William Norton. As he entered the room, Sophie looked up at his smiling face and silently thanked God that she didn't have to deal with that rude Dr. Higginbottom-man again. Sophie briefly tried to explain Little Bee's condition and what had happened to her, but Dr. Norton shared that he had already heard about the baby whose mother had died from ingesting rat poison. He also shared that the examining physician, Dr. Higginbotham, felt the baby would be dead in three or so days.

Sophie perked up and said, "Well, you see, doctor, she's very much alive, and this is day four. I think she's gonna make it. Yes, sir, I really do. Look here! See, her eyes are even open, and before, she didn't have the strength to open them. Also, her body is cooler now, but before, it was burning up with the fever."

Dr. Norton nodded and smiled, then told Sophie to lay Little Bee on the table so he could take a look at her. When she placed her on the table and Dr. Norton lifted the little oversized dress, there was an audible gasp as he looked down on the tiny, emaciated, and blackened body that still showed evidence of extensive internal hemorrhaging caused by the poison. He quickly tried to collect himself, but his hands trembled slightly as he grabbed the stethoscope to put it to her chest. He had been visibly shaken, and in all his medical practice had never seen anything like he was witnessing now. After several minutes of poking, prodding, taking temperature, and listening, Dr. Norton told Sophie she could take the baby off the table and hold her.

"Ma'am, I know your baby has survived past the time that Dr. Higginbotham said she would probably be dead, and that's a good thing. However, the poison has probably done extensive damage to her internal organs, and right now, it's hard to tell what negative effect that will have from here on out. My first suggestion is that you get a pillow a little longer than the length of her body, and when you have to carry her around, put her on the pillow before doing so. Since her body is so fragile and her skin paper thin, the pillow will help make her more comfortable. Also, she still has a fever, and the heat from your body only makes it worse for her.

"Second, I'm going to suggest that you take her to a private doctor rather than continue coming to the emergency room here or even visiting a clinic. This baby's condition is such that she needs to be seen by the same doctor each time she comes in rather than different doctors who have no knowledge of the circumstances surrounding her condition. I'll warn you that more than likely, it's going to be pretty expensive, so I hope you and your husband are prepared to shoulder the kind of expense her care will cost."

"Doctor, we are willing to do whatever it takes to get this baby well," Sophie responded.

With that assurance, Dr. Norton continued, "Your baby will need to have special medical tests done in order to determine the extent of damage the poison has done to her internal organs. She needs to be seen by someone who can keep track of her progress and who you can call immediately if there is a problem that needs to be addressed right away. You also need a doctor who is willing to make house calls if necessary. Therefore, I am going to refer you to a young Negro doctor I met a few weeks ago while attending a training at the Meharry Medical Center in Nashville.

"Lucky for you and your baby, that particular training seminar focused on children's diseases and health. Therefore, he will have more up-to-date medical knowledge regarding children than some of the other doctors here in Little Rock. His name is Dr. Jonathan Robinson, and he is a very bright and upcoming doctor. I believe his office is on Ninth Street, but I'll have the nurse get his address and phone number and bring it out to the waiting room for you.

"I will also give Dr. Robinson a call and briefly explain the circumstances and my preliminary findings. That way, he can do a bit of research and be prepared before he meets with you and your baby. Be sure to give him a call as soon as you can to set up an appointment because this baby needs medical attention right away. Meanwhile, keep doing whatever you have been doing over the past few days to get her to this point. I wish you the best with your little girl," he offered before pulling the curtain back and leaving the partition.

Unlike the first visit, Sophie felt encouraged. Dr. Norton had at least taken the time to examine Little Bee, then offered the name of another doctor who could possibly help her. To Sophie, it also meant that Dr. Norton felt Little Bee was going to make it. *Why else would he be sending her to another doctor if he thought she was just going to die in a few more days?* she thought. Sophie could hardly wait to get back to the waiting room to share the news with Miss Bertha and her daughter.

True to his word, Dr. Norton had given Dr. Robinson a call, and after giving him an overview of Bee's condition and the unusual circumstances surrounding her illness, Dr. Robinson immediately made the decision to see her. He was so intrigued by the fact that this baby was still alive in spite of everything she had been through that he did not wait for Sophie or Blake to call him, but rather gave them a call. He wanted to be able to take his time during their visit and not be rushed because of scheduled back-to-back appointments. Therefore, he arranged to see them the following Saturday morning. It was a Godsend since Blake was off that Saturday and could drive them to the appointment. It would also give him a chance to hear what the doctor had to say.

Three days later at 11:15 a.m., Sophie, Blake and Little Bee were sitting in Dr. Robinson's office. His office was located at 614 West Ninth Street, the area where many Negro businesses west of Main Street were located. This area was considered the hub of the Negro community. The entrance to 614 was a small doorway located between Ollie's Pool Hall and Watson's Barber Shop. A sign posted over the door to the narrow stairway leading to the second floor read:

Offices of Dr. Jonathan Robinson, Family Practice
Dr. Samuel Townsend, Optometry
Second Floor

When Sophie and Blake found their way to his second floor office, the door was locked. At first, they thought they had read the sign wrong, but after a couple of knocks, the door was opened by a man of medium build about five-feet-ten-inches tall, wearing thick bifocals and a huge smile. Dr. Robinson was nothing like Sophie had imagined him to be. He invited them in and gave Blake a firm handshake and Sophie a gentle pat on the back since she was holding Little Bee. Sophie had taken Dr. Norton's advice and was now carrying Little Bee on a pillow with a pillowcase she had made out of soft teddy bear print cotton.

While leading them back to his examination room, he explained that his receptionist did not work on Saturdays, so he was a "one-man show" today. Sophie loved the brightness of the office with sunlight streaming through the two large windows overlooking Ninth Street and immediately took a liking to Dr. Robinson. The brightness of the office and his warm manner immediately put her at ease. While taking her seat, she thought, *Huh, I definitely have come a long way from the crowded hospital and that ole Dr. Higginbottom or whatever his name was. Yeah, he was the bottom, all right. I'd even go way beyond that and say he was the pits.*

Dr. Robinson took his time examining Little Bee, all the while asking questions that Sophie tried as best she could to answer. He would stop to write something on a pad on the examination table, then continue the examination. Several times, he asked Sophie to assist him by turning Little Bee over, holding her up, keeping her mouth open, or keeping her head still as he looked into her eyes. Sophie noticed how careful he was being so that he wouldn't hurt her any more than he had to. She also noticed that he kept going back again and again to listen to her heart, moving the listening instrument from one side to the other and back again. *Oh, my Lord!*

thought Sophie. "What on earth is he listening for?" After what seemed like a lifetime, he told Sophie she could get Little Bee dressed.

All of a sudden, Sophie had a sinking feeling in the pit of her stomach and a dreaded feeling that what Dr. Robinson was about to say would not be good news. She also sensed that she and Blake were going to be facing an uphill battle that was bound to go on for a long time. Those feelings were soon confirmed as he started sharing his concerns, telling them what he thought the rat poison had possibly done to Little Bee's body.

"Mr. Blake and Miss Sophie, you've got one of the biggest challenges of your life lying ahead of you. Since talking to Dr. Norton, I've taken the time to do some research since I've never had a case where someone had ingested rat poison. Unfortunately, what I've found is not pretty. Let me begin by explaining how rat poison works.

"There are basically two types of rat poison available today, but the one most commonly used here in Arkansas contains arsenic, barium, and thallium. All of these ingredients are destructive, but perhaps the one that does the most harm to the body is arsenic. It's a miracle your baby has lasted this long. If her mother ingested enough poison to kill her within a few hours and the baby was nursing during that time, then she ingested quite a bit of the poison as well.

"Arsenic is an anticoagulant which does not allow the blood to clot, so the blackness of her skin is caused by her hemorrhaging or bleeding underneath the skin. At least we can see that, and it's obvious there has been a lot of hemorrhaging since her body is almost completely covered. The real problem, though, is that most of the damage has been done in areas we cannot see. For example, the poison attacks the central nervous system and causes swelling in the brain and problems with the spinal cord. Have you noticed the baby's body ever becoming rigid or stiff, or does she start making any jerking movements?"

"Yes, doctor! I almost forget to tell you, but a couple of times, she started acting like the people do when they're having fits and start foaming at the mouth," Sophie chimed in. "It kind of scared me at first, but then she seemed like she was okay, so I just let it pass. You know, she's dealing with so much that it's hard to remember everything I need to tell you. Oh yes, and she did stop breathing three times during the first couple of days after I took her from the plantation."

"Taking on a sick baby like this is no easy task," Dr. Robinson continued. "What's probably happening when it looks like she is having a fit is that she is suffering from brain hemorrhaging which is causing her to have seizures. I would guess there is also swelling which is building up pressure and could also be cutting off oxygen from certain parts of her brain.

"Adults experiencing this problem would have severe headaches and experience weakness on one side of the body. Unfortunately in Bee's case, she can't let us know what she's feeling, so we are left playing a guessing game and trying to figure out what's going on. If there is hemorrhaging in the brain, which I am inclined to believe because of the seizures, then there may be problems down the road with her development and her ability to learn. If so, then we'll just have to deal with that challenge when we get to it. Do you have other children?"

"No, we have not been so blessed," responded Blake as he lowered his head to hide the hurt and disappointment his face always showed when asked that question.

"Then, I am going to give you a list of guidelines I received during a training I attended last month. It tells what babies should be doing as they develop," Dr. Robinson continued. "For example, if the list says that between two and three months, she should be lifting her head when she is on her stomach, just ignore it.

"Your baby is so weak from fighting the effects of the poison and fighting for her life that there is no way she will be strong enough to be able to lift her head. However, if at four months, she starts to do some of the things that the chart says she should be doing at two months, then we know she is making progress. Keep a record of her progress so we can discuss it when you bring her in for her regular visits, and I can then place a note in her chart. Just remember, though, this list just gives suggestions of what she should be doing sometime in the future."

"Another major concern I have right now is her heart. During my examination, I detected some irregularities in her heartbeat. We call that arrhythmia. Unfortunately, arsenic attacks every organ in the body, including the cells of the heart, which interferes with its ability to function properly. Unlike the swelling in the brain, though, we now have a test we perform that can help us determine what's going on with her heart. It's called an electrocardiogram, or ECG for short.

"Don't worry. It doesn't hurt the baby, but it will tell us if there is a problem. I can set you up for an appointment, but you'll have to take her back to University Hospital since it is the only place in Little Rock that does the ECG. The test could be a little expensive, though. Do you happen to have any health insurance?"

"I think the folks in the Rock Island office said I can use my new health insurance starting August first since I began working for them the beginning of May," Blake responded. "Thank God for the union, which is now making Rock Island give Negroes health insurance," he continued. "They started taking out the $1.23 for the premiums last week, so it's coming about just in time to help our baby."

Dr. Robinson resumed giving more information to Sophie and Blake. "Another problem with arsenic is that it can eat away at the membrane that lines the stomach and cause lacerations or tears in the stomach and the intestines. Miss Sophie, have you noticed bloody stools or diarrhea in her diaper? Miss Sophie? Miss Sophie!" Dr. Robinson asked, speaking louder now as he touched her arm.

"Oh, oh, I'm sorry doctor, but all this stuff you're saying is just scaring me because it sounds like Little Bee's got a whole lot of problems. I don't know how this baby can deal with all this stuff because she's been through so much already," Sophie responded hesitantly as she tried to wrap her mind around all that Dr. Robinson was sharing. "Now, what were you asking me?" Sophie inquired.

"I was asking if the baby has bloody stools or diarrhea in her diaper," Dr. Robinson repeated.

"Oh yes, sir, doctor," Sophie began. "In fact, ever since we got her, she's had bloody everything. Even before we started feeding her with the dropper, she had blood on the folded rags we laid her on while we were trying to get the poison out of her body. Yesterday, it seemed to have gotten a little better though."

"Miss Sophie, what do you mean about feeding her with the dropper?" Dr. Robinson inquired.

"Well, you see, she's too weak to suck on the bottle Miss Bertha tried to give her. So, we've been boiling up some cow's milk, putting a little sugar in it, and feeding her by filling up the dropper and squeezing a little milk into her mouth," Sophie proudly informed him.

"Well, I must say that's quite ingenious," Dr. Robinson said admiringly, "and apparently, it's working because she is producing stools even if they are runny. How often do you feed her and about how much milk do you give her with each feeding?" Dr. Robinson continued to inquire, and Sophie was trying to remember and answer as best she could, but she was noticeably getting tired and a bit anxious. Dr. Robinson noticed it, too, and assured her she could give him that information on their next visit.

Picking up his pad, Dr. Robinson stared at the notes for quite some time without looking at or speaking to Blake or Miss Sophie. He sat making some more notations, and all was quiet for a few minutes. Suddenly, he laid his pad down, and in a voice barely above a whisper, he said, "Miss Sophie, I'm afraid I need to have you put your baby back on the examining table for just a couple more minutes." Sophie's heart began racing as she realized something was not right about this change in direction and the change in his voice. How could the news get any worse, and how could Little Bee deal with any more problems? She reckoned she would soon find out.

Dr. Robinson tried to maintain a steadiness in his voice as his brain and professional knowledge screamed heart and respiratory complications, two of the deadliest diseases anyone can have, and here they were talking about a ten-day-old baby fighting for her life. Lord, help her …

NINE

Mountains and Meadows

O nce I decided to move ahead with the research and writing the paper that I would submit as my end-of-the-year project, I immediately started making plans to do the research and gather material I'd need during my spring break. I planned to use the seven days I had off to conduct interviews with Nanna, Dad, and anyone else who could help shed some light and provide information crucial to what I needed for the paper. Now, I realized that I had opened Pandora's Box and was feeling uneasy about where all of this was heading. Yet I knew I had made the right decision.

The idea had never crossed my mind that the process would be so emotionally draining. Hearing the details about Nanna Bee's mother and how she was murdered by her husband's girlfriend was almost beyond anything I could have imagined. I was reluctant to continue asking Nanna questions about her poisoning and what she had gone through after they had only given her three days to live. I was now getting a *glimpse of why Nanna had always started to cry when she reached a certain part of the little bit of information she had shared with me and my sisters. Several times during the interview, Nanna had asked for a break, and I had been happy to oblige because I badly needed one as well. I knew the next few hours would be even more difficult for Nanna as they progressed in the story, so I braced himself for what was coming.*

I tried to tape Nanna's interview sessions using my cell phone but soon realized I needed a recording device with ample storage capacity. I also needed something that would allow me to keep the records for years to come. These interviews, which had started out as a project, had become far more important. This was Nanna voicing her story, and I wanted to preserve these recordings so they could be passed down to future generations: my children, nieces, nephews, and so on.

Up to this point, I had gathered a ton of background information from Nanna. However, I now felt I needed to move in a more specific direction to determine how all of this related to my dad. But before I could get started on the next segment of questions, Nanna shocked me by saying, "Michael, you're trying to gather material to prepare for your end-of-the-year project, and I know this assignment is extremely important to you. However, I am only going to allow you to ask me one more question. Being the teacher that I was and still am, I never pass up a teachable moment or an opportunity to challenge my students. I know, I know, you're not my student, but you know your Nanna," she said with a sly smile.

"So, young man, you had better put your thinking cap on

and formulate a question that opens the door for you to garner the specific information you need for your project. Oh, and by the way, the question has to be a simple, straight-forward question—not one that takes up an entire page and has fifty-million parts to it." She then leaned back in her chair, folded her arms, and smiled that I-bet-I-got-you-now smile.

I sat there stunned, my mouth still partially open from attempting to say something as Nanna was laying out the conditions for the rest of the interview but knowing better than to try to butt in or cut her off because she would never tolerate that. My mind began racing wildly, thinking of all the questions I had spent hours formulating so I would get the kind of responses I was looking for. Now, she was throwing a monkey wrench at me and destroying my entire modus operandi. It took a minute or so for her words to sink in. How on earth was I going to get all the information I needed by asking just one more question?

Then, my adrenalin kicked in. I had always liked a good challenge. I could remember an instance when my teacher had given an assignment with so many restrictions and conditions that it seemed almost impossible to get the assignment done. Yet, my classmates and I had risen to the occasion and with such great results that even the teacher was impressed. Now, Nanna was doing something quite similar, pushing me into a corner where I had better probe correctly, or I would not get the most crucial bits of information I needed. "Alright Nanna," I said with feigned confidence, "give me a minute to collect my thoughts, and I'll come up with one heck of a good question. In fact, it will be better than any question your students have ever written."

After several minutes of scribbling notes, letting out sighs along with one "Ah, Nanna," crossing out words, rubbing his hands together, and rearranging phrases, I was finally satisfied with my question. "Okay, Nanna, here goes," I stated with a bit of hesitancy. "What experiences in your past made you want to adopt my dad, and what enabled you to have the love, patience, and determination to hang in there with him when most people would have given up and returned him to the adoption agency?"

Now, it was Nanna's turn to be stunned. There was dead silence for what seemed like eons before she finally managed to say softly, "Wow, grandson, you have far exceeded my expectations, but then I should have known. They didn't just let you waltz your way into the school you're attending without you having something going on upstairs," she said smilingly. "With that question, you will get all the information you'll need for your project ... and possibly more."

As I was getting his recording device set up for the next session, I realized that Nanna's restriction on numerous questions had forced the interview in a direction where I would gather pertinent information I needed. With everything now in place, I nodded for her to begin speaking again.

"Looking back over my life, I can definitely say that if I had not had such a tenuous beginning and had not been given the adopted parents God blessed me with, I would not have become the person I grew up to be. I spent so much of my early childhood fighting the devastating effects of the poisoning, and in the process, my parents spent a ton of money as well. They were not the ones who brought me into this world and, technically speaking, had no obligation to me whatsoever.

Yet they loved and stood by me in spite of my many challenges. They met those challenges physically, emotionally, and financially.

"Without them demonstrating that kind of unconditional love and day-after-day-after-day commitment, I don't know if I would have been motivated to hang in there with your dad. But knowing how my parents sacrificed and did everything humanly possible to keep me alive and give me a chance to become healthy again, how could I not pay it forward? They were the perfect role models. As for your dad, not only was he the most difficult child I had ever encountered, but his behavior even confounded the experts: the social workers, psychologist, psychiatrist, nurses, doctors, pastors, teachers, principals, judges, counselors, policemen, firemen, you name it."

"What? Are you serious, Nanna?" I asked with disbelief written all over my face. "Growing up, I would often hear bits and pieces about Dad's antics, and my mom often says she has no idea how you managed to get him to adulthood without strangling him or losing your mind," I added kiddingly. "I had no idea, though, that it was that bad."

"Yes, he was a *pistol* as we would say in the South. And you'll probably be even more shocked when you hear more about some of the things he was able to pull off. In fact, people used to tell me that if I ever wrote a book about it, readers would swear I made it up. You know, though, sometimes truth is stranger than fiction, and in your dad's case, I could not have made up some of the stuff he did."

"I know where you get your smarts from, though, because as a little boy, your dad would run rings around his dad and me as well as other adults who worked with him. Plainly put, he would out-think us, then turn around and out-smart and out-maneuver us. More often than not, by the time we all finally figured out what he was up to, he had slam-dunked us and sprinted off looking to score his next basket, a three-pointer this time. But, whoa, I'm getting way ahead of myself. Let me back up and put things in some kind of chronological order so it will make more sense to you."

"I guess I should start by telling you that Sophie and Blake officially adopted me on June 17, 1943. I have no idea how they got Lou to agree to the adoption, but knowing how tenacious Sophie was, I'm sure she was quite persuasive, and he didn't have much of a choice."

"I have vague memories of things hurting me, and I associate that pain with a certain smell. I think it's some type of liniment, and to this day, I can't stand that smell. Pain aside, my first real memory was sort of a happy one. It was Christmastime. Daddy had come in to wake me up and tell me that Santa Claus had come to visit during the night. Since I had trouble walking, rather than putting on my braces, he picked me up and carried me into the living room. Muh Dear, that's what I called my great-aunt Sophie, was standing in front of the biggest Christmas tree imaginable with a huge smile on her face. The tree was so tall it went from floor to ceiling and covered the entire front window. There were tons of light on it and so many presents underneath that there was no room to walk around it without stepping on them.

"I must have been about four or five years old. I had been asking Santa to bring me a doll with long curly hair, a toy stove and icebox—which is what they used to call refrigerators back then—and a tricycle. Most of all, I wanted the tricycle. I can remember being so excited and wanting to open the presents right then and there, but Muh Dear said I couldn't open them until we came home from Early Mass. I have no idea why they called it Early Mass when it really was a Christmas sunrise service at Collins Street Baptist Church in the east end of Little Rock and had absolutely nothing to do with masses celebrated at the Catholic or Lutheran churches.

"Following the service, Daddy and Muh Dear invited some of their friends to our house for Christmas breakfast and to watch me open my presents. This was a special treat for their friends because they were in their fifties and sixties, and most had no children, or if they had, they were grown and living somewhere out of state. I can remember just tearing the paper off the presents as fast as I could and sitting there screaming and bouncing up and down.

"When I finished opening the presents, Muh Dear and Daddy told me to close my eyes. Daddy then went into their bedroom and got my biggest gift. When I was told to open my eyes, there Daddy stood holding the handle of a beige and red wooden Coaster wagon. I can remember being so disappointed and saying, 'I didn't ask Santa for a wagon. I told him I wanted a tricycle! Why didn't Santa bring my tricycle?'

"I saw the smile disappear from Daddy's face, and even though I didn't know it then, I'm sure Daddy and Muh Dear's feelings must have been hurt. Daddy dropped the handle of the wagon and came over to kneel down beside me. 'Baby, Santa wanted to bring you that tricycle, but he knew it would be too hard for you to pedal with the braces on your legs,' he responded as he gently rubbed my back.

"'Besides, with your wagon, you can just sit there and ride along while your mom and I do all the work pulling you around the neighborhood. The other kids can't do that because they've got to pedal themselves around,' he added with a chuckle. I later found out that most of the other kids close to my age in the neighborhood had either gotten tricycles or bicycles for Christmas. I cried for a couple of days. I think that was the first time I felt like I was different from other children.

"I can also remember that every Sunday when we had Sunday School, which was held in the basement of our church, I couldn't just run down the stairs to my classroom. Daddy would have to carry me down, then come back and get me when the class was over. I would also get winded easily, so most of the time, I would just sit on the sideline if the other kids were playing ball, tag, or hide-and-go-seek. Sometimes, it was really hard for me to breathe, even when I wasn't moving around. Oh, by the way, Michael, now that you have come up with your major question, feel free to ask me to clarify something if you don't understand it."

"Okay, Nanna, but so far, I'm good," I responded as I hastily made some more notes on the yellow legal pad I had been using since starting the interview yesterday. As long as I could remember, Nanna had always been this healthy, vibrant person, and even though she was now in her seventies, she had not seemed to slow down much at all. I could remember when my sisters and I were little, Nanna would come and pick us up and take us to her house for the weekend.

Many times, she would pack us into her SUV and take us to the zoo, parks, swimming, and hiking up in the mountains, and she never seemed to get tired. Now, I was getting a totally different picture of Nanna as a frail, weak, and sickly young child who was told she would probably be that way most of her life. That picture was in complete contrast to the woman I knew. How on earth had she been able to make the transition? *I wondered. I hoped that while answering the one question she had allowed me to ask, she would answer that question as well, or perhaps I might sneak in that question when asking for clarification.*

"I think learning to play the piano was a life saver for me in more ways than one. It all started after the Christmas tricycle incident. Muh Dear felt badly about me not being able to run and play outdoors. All day, she would watch me stay in the house, stand, stare out the window or the front screen door, and look at the other kids while they played in their yards. Sometimes, I would sit on the front porch and play by myself with my toys, and once in a while, one of the neighbor kids would come over and play jacks with me.

"So, one night, I heard Muh Dear tell Daddy that they needed to find something else for me to do that would be fun but wouldn't require a lot of physical exertion. That's when she suggested they try to find someone to give me piano lessons. 'We've got that big ole piano just sitting there in the living room, and sometimes Bee will go over there and just start playing on the keys. You know Lou is one heck of a musician, so maybe he passed some of his talent on down to her,' she informed Daddy.

"'You know, Pet,' Daddy responded, 'now that her medical bills are a little less than when we first started out, maybe we could use the money you get from doing the Sanders' family laundry every week to pay for her lessons.'

"Two weeks after that conversation, I was on my way to Ms. Campbell's house for my first piano lesson. I remember when I first saw her, I thought, *This lady has to be a hundred years old.* Her house was really stuffy and dark, and the windows were covered by heavy drapes that didn't allow any sunlight into the room. The only light came from a small table lamp that sat near the door of the piano room, and the other from the lamp she had sitting on top of the piano so I could see the music.

"Even though I didn't like her very much, I loved being able to learn how to play the piano. I can still remember Ms. Campbell sitting beside the piano on this little velvet chair with pink and blue flowers, eating some smelly old cheese with crackers, and hitting my knuckles with the ruler every time I played a wrong note. She also didn't like the fact that I could play by ear and play tunes that I had only heard once. She tried to convince Muh Dear that letting me make up tunes or play tunes I had heard instead of reading the actual music was bad for me. She said I would never be a good musician if I was allowed to continue doing things like that.

"Thank goodness Muh Dear didn't listen to her and allowed me to make up all the songs I wanted when I played at home. She just admonished me to make sure I only played the exact notes written on the music page when I went for my lessons so I wouldn't end up with sore knuckles."

"About six months after I had started piano lessons, Muh Dear started to notice that the muscles in my hands and arms were getting stronger. In fact, she often brought jars to me that she was having trouble opening. She shared this information with Daddy, and they started to concoct a plan. Daddy reasoned that if the exercise and use of the muscles I used to play the piano were making my arms, hands, and fingers stronger, so perhaps they could come up with some similar exercises to make my legs stronger.

"The next day, instead of putting my braces on immediately when I got out of bed in the morning, they allowed me to walk around my bed holding on to the bedposts and Muh Dear's hand for support. At first, I was real wobbly, but then I got better. This began a daily ritual that gradually expanded to walking around the entire bedroom, then out into the hall, and finally around the entire house for longer periods of time.

"I can still remember the first day I was able to walk out onto the porch without using braces or Muh Dear's arm for support. It was such a special day for all of us. Muh Dear stood there looking at me with this huge smile on her face as tears rolled down her cheeks. Later that evening after Daddy got home from work, she shared the good news with him. After dinner, we celebrated by sitting on the front porch swing and glider, eating delicious homemade ice cream Muh Dear had made using peaches from the tree in our backyard."

"That day was the beginning of me moving toward becoming a normal child. Soon after, I was able to go without braces for most of the time. During the party celebrating my sixth birthday that summer, Muh Dear and Daddy surprised me with the tricycle I had so desperately wanted that Christmas. Even though most of the neighborhood kids had graduated to bicycles with training wheels, I didn't care. I now had something to ride up and down the sidewalk like the other kids.

"Our neighborhood was located on a slight incline, so

going downhill made the pedaling a little easier. Even so, I lagged behind many times because I could not pedal as fast nor did I have the stamina. Yet I felt like I belonged. Still battling the asthma problem, though, I would have to stop often to catch my breath. My friends got used to it and would hang around and wait for me. To this day, I remember it being one of the best summers of my childhood."

TEN

Developing Character

"Muh Dear learned the hard way the pitfalls of spoiling a child early in life. From the day she brought me into their home, I became the center of their universe. It's funny how babies and infants pick up on that right away, and regardless of whether they are sick or well, they can manage to wrap their parents around their little fingers.

"Now, it was hitting her like a ton of bricks that I had become a little 'spoiled brat' monster. She told me that she and Daddy would have long discussions about this, and even though Daddy was all for just letting me have my way to make up for everything I had been through, Muh Dear was starting to put her foot down and say no to my demands, hissy fits, and temper tantrums. As I continued to grow stronger and able to do more for longer periods of time, she started looking for ways to help develop my character and started teaching me to think about others rather than just myself.

"She began with first things first. There was no doubt that my survival had been a miracle, and Muh Dear wanted to make certain I knew the source of that miracle. Saturday nights in our home were family prayer nights, and everything stopped in its track when 9:00 p.m. rolled around.

"Initially, I didn't understand the significance of that prayer time and dreaded it because that was the time the western, *Hop-Along Cassidy*, aired on the radio. If prayer time lasted past 9:30, then I would also miss most of *Jubilee*, a radio program that featured Negro singers and musicians. I would wait all week to hear the singers belting out songs that were so different from the music they usually played. So, not only would I be upset that prayer time was making me miss my programs, but it was also boring.

"Prayer time always began with us singing either 'Jesus Keep Me Near the Cross' or 'Sweet Hour of Prayer.' This would be followed by Daddy reading the Ten Commandments, and would you believe that to this day, I can still recite the Commandments by memory? After the scripture reading, I would say the Lord's Prayer. Daddy would follow me with his prayer, thanking the Lord for blessing them with me, and asking for health and protection for his family. When he would end his prayer, Muh Dear would take over.

"She always prayed last. It was like she had been saving up all week for this prayer time and had made a laundry list of everything she wanted to say to the Lord. Now that Saturday night had finally arrived, she could just go down that list checking everything off. Muh Dear would pray so long sometimes that both Daddy and I would fall asleep, and sometimes he would snore. For the longest time, I could not understand why most of Muh Dear's prayers would be about me, and many times, she would start to sob, and her whole body would even begin to shake. I can remember once Muh Dear cried so hard that she could not finish her prayer or even get up off her knees, so Daddy and I had to go over and help her.

"I later learned that she was deathly ill. She was crying out to the Lord to help her get well again so that she could continue to raise and take care of me and that I would not end up losing another mother.

"As I look back on those Saturday nights, I am amazed at the positive influence they have had on my life, but that was not always the case. I can remember plotting ways to endure prayer time and entertain myself while Muh Dear was praying. So, I got smart, I thought, and started hiding candy and other goodies underneath the cushion of the big armchair where I always knelt. After finishing my prayer, I would pull out the candy or cookie and enjoy my treats while she prayed. It wasn't until I was much older that I truly understood the power of her prayers and realized that the answer to those prayers had come in the form of my miracles, my survival, and my excellent health.

"Muh Dear had been talking to Daddy about letting me join a Girl Scout troop because she thought it would be good for me to meet, socialize, and do projects with other girls my age. However, she found out that because I was only seven years old, I was too young to become a Girl Scout. It was then that she started searching for a Brownie troop which was designed for girls ages six through eight.

"She soon realized there were no Brownie troops in the south end of Little Rock. Being the tenacious person she was,

Muh Dear decided to become a troop leader and start her own Brownie troop. At the time, I was completely unaware that she could barely read and write. She had dropped out of school in third grade to pick cotton and help her family with other farming chores after her father died. Yet she was determined not to let that stop her. So, one day, Muh Dear drove downtown to the Girl Scout office and picked up an application. Daddy helped her complete it and other paperwork needed to become a troop leader.

"Once she received her certificate and the orientation packet from the Girl Scout headquarters, Daddy helped her read and study the material so she could organize and develop activities for the group. She memorized the Girl Scout pledge so that she could teach it to us and not have to stumble over the words as she tried to read them. She also asked Miss Alberta, one of our neighbors who was a schoolteacher, and Miss Tennyson from our church to help with the group. Ms. Alberta's daughter, Rosemary, who was too old to be a Brownie, also helped with games, teaching us songs, and serving refreshments.

"I remember the day of our first Brownie meeting. I was so excited when four other girls came to our house and said they wanted to become Brownies. Betty, Rosalyn, Rosie, Dorothy, and I became the first Brownies in our troop. At our first meeting, we learned the Girl Scout pledge. I felt so important when we were told to raise our right hand, touch our thumb and little fingers together while leaving the remaining three fingers sticking up in the air as we recited, 'On my honor, I will try to serve God and my country and to help people at all times.'

"We were told we would be doing a lot of service projects where we would go and help people who were sick, elderly, or in need because of a death in the family or losing their home and belongings due to a fire. The best part, though, was when we all held hands and sang a song at the end of the meeting before having cookies and punch.

"By the time we finally got our Brownie uniforms, there were twelve girls in our troop. It was a summer day in June, and Muh Dear and Miss Alberta had planned an outing for us to celebrate getting our new uniforms. We were a sight to behold in our brown-belted shirt dresses and brown beanie caps as we left our house and walked the two blocks to the bus stop.

"We boarded the bus for downtown, took our seats in the back—which was the only place Negroes could sit—and exited the bus in front of Pfeiffer Department Store on South Main Street. Muh Dear and Miss Alberta were smartly dressed in their green button-up Girl Scout leader dresses with yellow neckerchiefs and matching green hats. They lined us up in single file, and we proudly walked the five blocks to the Conrow Home for the Aged where we sang and passed out candy.

"As we walked by, people on the sidewalk and even some in cars passing by smiled, waved, clapped, cheered, and honked their horns. I was even more shocked when some of the white people we passed smiled and clapped and told us how nice we looked. We felt so proud. This was the first time in my life I had ever had people clap for me for just walking down the street, and I knew that being a Brownie was something very special.

"That was the first of many service projects we did over the next year and a half, but none of the others were as exciting as that very first one. I think it was also the first time I really became aware of how important it is to be concerned about and help others and the great feeling you get from doing so.

"Muh Dear also used the Brownies as an opportunity to teach me responsibility and goal setting. Every summer, there was a Girl Scouts Camp that ran for a week. This was an opportunity to go away from home and spend a week meeting other Brownies and Girl Scouts, learning new skills, having fun, and sharing memories. However, many girls could not go because of the camp fee.

"Muh Dear and Daddy sat down and helped me map out a plan with a timeline for selling enough cookies to earn my camp fee. I knew exactly how many boxes of cookies I had to sell to cover the fee, and if I wanted spending money, then I had to sell even more. I can remember asking Daddy and Muh Dear to help me, and even gave both of them the number of boxes I needed for them to sell. My territory was to sell cookies to people in our neighborhood, at our church, and to ask my uncle Lem and his wife, Aunt Vinney, to sell cookies at the church they pastored.

"Daddy was responsible for selling boxes down at the Rock Island Railroad Station where he worked and to people whose grass he cut on weekends. Muh Dear was assigned to take boxes to her Sunshine Club, Eastern Star, and the National Council of Negro Women meetings. At that time, we only had one flavor—the shortbread cookies—but it didn't matter. I sold so many cookies that I not only paid for my summer camp fee but had enough left over to buy some clothes for camp and have some spending money too.

"My first big test came when Muh Dear found out that one of the other girls in our troop hadn't been able to raise enough money to cover her camp fee. Even though Brenita had tried, she was from a single parent home and had not been given the help and support that many of the other girls had received. Therefore, she had only been able to sell enough cookies to cover about one-third of the camp fee. Her mother was not able to pay the additional amount needed, so she would not be able to go.

"Muh Dear presented me with my first big decision. She told me about Brenita's situation and said if I wanted, I could donate some of my extra money to her so that she would be able to go. However, it would mean that I would have less money to spend on clothes for camp and for things I would want to buy at camp.

"At first, I hesitated because I wanted to have as much money to spend as a lot of the other kids, especially kids like Marilyn and Bobbie whose parents I thought were rich. Then, I realized that by thinking of others rather than just myself, I could share my money and give another girl an opportunity to also go to camp. That was one of the best decisions I made during my childhood. Brenita and I were able to share a cabin together at camp, and just seeing her face light up as we participated in all of the fun activities made it the best part of my camping experience.

"Little did I know that that experience and similar experiences during my childhood were laying the foundation and creating in me a burning desire to help others and make a positive difference in their lives.

"Muh Dear apparently designated me as the volunteer child of the south end. As I progressed with my piano-playing skills, she began volunteering me to play for Sunday school at our church, then graduated to the young adult choir, and finally to helping Ms. Montique with the entire church service. Later on, I was asked to provide music at the Sunshine Club's annual tea and functions for other club activities throughout the city.

"These volunteer acts gave me the experience I needed to become accompanist for my junior high and senior high school choral groups and eventually led to paid positions at several different churches where I remained until I went away to school. Several of these organizations selected me as the recipient of their scholarship awards, and several churches presented me with financial gifts when it was time for me to go away to college.

"Regardless of whether I was doing volunteer work or work on jobs for which I was compensated, the rules Muh Dear and Daddy set for me were the same. 'Always be prepared before you show up for a job and get there a few minutes early so you can begin on time. Once you arrive, give 150%. Don't just do enough to get by. Ask questions if you don't understand the assignment. Stay until you finish the assignment you have been given for that day, even if it means working a little bit later. If and when you decide to leave a position for whatever reason, always leave on good terms. Never, ever, burn bridges because you don't know what the future holds. There may come a time when you might have to cross back over that bridge, and if you've burned it, you're out of options.'

"That advice paid off big time during my senior year of high school. When I was in seventh grade, Muh Dear got the bright idea that I should get a newspaper route and start delivering newspapers to people's homes.

"My first thought was *Muh Dear, have you lost your mind? Don't you realize I am a big-time student in junior high school now, and what girl has a paper route when they're in junior high school?* Nevertheless, Muh Dear was persistent and stood her ground. So, I started soliciting sales for *The State Press*, a newspaper developed specifically to keep the Negro community informed about important social, civic, and political issues.

"The paper was owned by Mr. L. C. and Mrs. Daisy Bates. During my seventh and eighth grade years, I built a large customer base, delivered the papers, and also formed a close relationship with the Bates. Mrs. Bates was also instrumental in getting Muh Dear involved with the NAACP since she was the Arkansas State president.

"Once I entered high school and became involved with numerous extra-curricular activities that included accompanying the high school choir, I had very little time for anything else, including delivering *The State Press*, so my interaction with Mr. and Mrs. Bates and *The State Press* ended, or so I thought.

"Michael, before I continue, I am going to alert you that you are going to get a brief history lesson about a significant event that your nanna was involved in when I was sixteen and seventeen years old."

"Okay, Nanna, sounds interesting, and I love history anyway. I'm intrigued that you were part of a significant historical event. Do tell me more!" I responded while smiling and rubbing my hands together.

"I'm sure you are aware of the 1954 Supreme Court's decision in *Brown v. Board of Education of Topeka* that declared segregation in public schools unconstitutional. Up until that time, schools in the United States were segregated, and I grew up attending those segregated schools.

"Following the decision, school districts throughout the country were required to begin the process of integration. In response to this decision along with pressure from the Arkansas State NAACP of which Mrs. Bates was president, the Little Rock Board of Education devised a plan where integration of schools would take place over a period of time, starting with the high schools in September 1957.

"One day during the spring of 1957, Mrs. Bates called my house and asked to speak to Muh Dear. Later that evening after Daddy had gotten home, she came for a visit. She explained that she was in the process of identifying students who she thought might be good candidates for helping to integrate Central High School and would like for my parents to consider letting me participate.

"She felt that I had done such a great job delivering papers that I had a strong work ethic, had good people skills because I got along well with others, and because of the size of my customer base, was a member of the National Honor Society at school which meant I had the grades and the ability, and I was dependable. Who would have thought that my suffering through delivering those newspapers would have led to this?

Anyway, she left after asking them to consider letting me be involved but did stress the dangers and risks of doing so.

"The next morning, I was not surprised to hear Muh Dear on the phone telling Mrs. Bates that she and Daddy felt it was much too dangerous for me to be involved, that their top priority was to protect me, and that they were declining the offer. Later, Muh Dear told me that Mrs. Bates had been disappointed but understood.

"Needless to say, the 1957–1958 school year was a tumultuous year, and one that was not only emotionally and psychologically draining but challenged every belief I had ever had. Day after day, I sat on the living room floor glued to our little black-and-white television set while vicariously experiencing the Little Rock Nine's historic journey as they integrated Central High School.

"Still vivid in my mind after all these years are pictures of the Arkansas National Guard blocking my former classmates from entering the school building. I remember crying, then getting angry as Elizabeth Eckford walked alone clutching her notebook while women ran up behind her jeering, screaming, and spitting on her.

"I sat there in shock and thought, *How could adults who were probably parents themselves do this to someone else's child?* The images didn't stop there but continued throughout the school year with Federal Paratroopers escorting the nine students in and out of the building each day. The rioters in front of Central High School forced the nine students to be secretly evacuated while fearing for their lives. Newscasters gave morning to evening 'Breaking News' coverage.

"Many days in our classes at Horace Mann High School,

the all-black high school where we, including the nine students now at Central High, had attended up to that time, had trouble focusing on our lessons because of all the turmoil. We were dealing with a new normal. It was the longest nine months of our lives. Finally, in May 1958, there was something to celebrate! I remember jumping up and down, cheering, and shouting as Ernest Green joined the line of graduates and received his diploma from Central High School. He was a sight to behold!

"At that moment, I realized that many times in order to bring about change and improve conditions for the good of many, a few must make tremendous sacrifices. To this day, I have the utmost respect for the nine students who paved the way for my children and grandchildren to enjoy educational opportunities that we didn't have prior to them and their families making the sacrifices they made.

"The following September, which should have been the beginning of my senior year at Horace Mann and the second year of the Little Rock high school integration process, the high schools never opened. Caving to pressure from pro-segregation groups, Governor Orval Faubus signed a bill giving him power to close any school in Arkansas, and on September 18, 1958, he did just that.

"He attempted to halt the integration process by closing all the high schools in Little Rock. My fellow classmates and I along with our parents were stunned. What on earth were we going to do? How could he just take away our senior year, the year we had waited all our lives to experience? More importantly, though, what were we going to do now about our education?

"It was obvious what the white community was going to do. For the most part, they had the money and the resources to send their children to private schools or to schools outside of Little Rock or even out of state. And who knows? They may have even been forewarned of the intention to close the schools. Not so with most of us.

"I can still remember Muh Dear and Daddy frantically calling and asking for help from family, friends, neighbors, church members, anyone they could think of, but to no avail. September came and went, October came and went, and I had just resigned myself to finding a job and working through the year.

"Then, one day in November out of the clear blue, Muh Dear gets a call from Mrs. Bates asking if they had been able to get me into a school somewhere. When Muh Dear told her no, she told her she would get back to her within twenty-four hours but to start getting me ready because she may have a solution to my problem. Within two hours, Mrs. Bates called back and told Muh Dear to have me ready to leave by noon the next day.

"Apparently, she had contacted one of her dear friends in Connecticut whose husband had been president of one of the largest electric power utility companies in the country, and the lady had agreed to sponsor either two girls or two boys and give them the opportunity to finish the school year while living with her.

"The next day as I boarded the plane in Little Rock heading for New York where our sponsor would meet us, I couldn't help but reflect back over what my parents had always stressed while I was growing up: 'Always do your best and be sure you don't burn bridges because you never know when you may need to cross back over that bridge.' I was so thankful that I had heeded their advice and done my best to sell the newspapers I absolutely did not want to sell.

"My parents' foresightedness paid off in many ways, and the values they instilled in me remain with me to this day. Muh Dear may have only had a third-grade education, but that didn't stop her or slow her down. She had this saying that reflected her philosophy to a tee: 'You can't go around acting like you don't have a lick 'o sense. You've got to use the good common sense the Good Lord gave you when you're doing stuff.'

"Believe me, she lacked formal schooling, but she certainly was a student of life and caring, thus she was incredibly smart."

ELEVEN

The Adoption

"Michael, I know I've given you a ton of background information up to this point, but from here on out, I will be focusing on your dad. You are going to learn things about him that you never knew. Some are good, some funny, some scary, and, unfortunately, some of it is not so good. However, when you put them all together, the sum is your dad.

"On Tuesday, June 14, 1977, Terrance James 'TJ' entered our lives. Dave and I had been working with the adoption agency for over a year trying to qualify and meet the criteria that would get us approved to become adoptive parents. Because we already had a biological daughter, we wanted to adopt a little boy to give our daughter, Lynn, a little brother.

"Initially, our interest in adopting had come about after we had difficulty getting pregnant, and after six years of trying, we were getting anxious and frustrated. Fortunately, during our seventh year of marriage, we were finally pregnant, and after a very difficult pregnancy gave birth to our daughter Lynn on April 15, 1969. Six years following Lynn's birth, Dave and I found ourselves in a similar situation.

"Even though I had gotten pregnant a couple of times during that six-year period, I had difficulty carrying the baby to term and experienced a couple of miscarriages. Because I had been adopted and given a chance to have a good and productive life, I thought, *Why not give another child the same opportunity?* Thankfully, Grandpa Dave was on the same page, so we began searching for an adoption agency that would help us fulfill our dream of expanding our family.

"Three weeks after making the decision to adopt, we were sitting in a room with twelve other couples attending an adoption orientation meeting. The process sounded long and arduous with mountain-loads of paperwork to submit and interviews and required visits that seemed endless. Nevertheless, Dave and I were excited and willing to do whatever it would take to get our son. We realized immediately that meeting some of the requirements was going to be difficult due to the fact that Dave's employer had him working on a long-term project on the East Coast, and that would probably continue for the next ten to twelve months.

"His work schedule required him to fly out early every Monday morning and return home late Friday evenings. Our biggest challenge was that most of the interviews and home visits to determine our eligibility required both of us to be present at those meetings. The visits and meetings were conducted by Illinois State or Cook County government agents and usually took place during the week. Since most government offices were closed on weekends when Dave was in town, the process dragged on for almost a year.

"Meanwhile, based on the profile we had submitted to the adoption agency regarding the child we wanted to adopt, three little boys became eligible for adoption. However, since we had not completed all of the requirements, we were unable to adopt any of those boys. Can you imagine how different things would have turned out if we had already completed the process and adopted any of the other little boys? Some people may refer to it as luck that your dad was the first little boy to become available once we had been approved. I say it was divine intervention.

"Dave and I were invited to come down to the adoption agency and meet with Mr. Tony McIntosh, the social worker in charge of our adoption. He told us a little three-year-old boy had become eligible for adoption several weeks prior, but that a couple of families who were ahead of us on the list had declined the placement. They felt he didn't fit the profile of the boy they were looking to adopt. Mr. McIntosh said he could set up a meeting within seven days if we were interested in visiting with the little boy. Without hesitation, we said we would love to meet him.

"Mr. McIntosh said he could definitely arrange the meeting, but before we continued, he wanted to share some background information that might affect our decision as to whether we would want to proceed or not. He began, 'First, I want you to know that this little boy, Terrance James, who I'm going to refer to as TJ, has been in the system since he was four months old. From what I've been told, his mother had a severe drug problem and would go off and leave him and his three siblings by themselves for long periods of time. Apparently, Child Protective Services found out about this and removed all four of the kids from the home and placed them in Foster Care. We later learned that the mother had died from an overdose and the whereabouts of his father is unknown.

"'The picture I am going to paint for you regarding TJ's time in the Foster Care system is not a pretty one. TJ's first placement was in a foster home on Chicago's south side. From all appearances, this family was only interested in the money that the State of Illinois would reimburse to them for providing care for TJ. An unexpected visit to the home by one of the Child Protective Services agents several months after TJ's placement showed flagrant violations of the Foster Care Contract and threats to his well-being.

"'The agent recommended that TJ be removed immediately after finding overwhelming evidence that he was being severely beaten, abused, and neglected. During a visit by the social worker to the second foster home placement, one of the older girls told her that TJ was being picked on by a couple of the older boys. She said she told the foster mother about it, but she did nothing. She even told the worker to look for scars or wounds that the boys had inflicted on him.

"'TJ was removed and placed in a third home, and again, he was abused and neglected. Not only was he not being fed properly, but once the meal was over, a lock was placed on the refrigerator to prevent him from eating later. Apparently, the lock was placed there after TJ slipped downstairs late one night and ate an entire package of frozen hot dogs because he was so hungry.

"'A visiting social worker noticed TJ's bloated stomach,

and when she took him outside and asked if he was hungry, he told her that he was always hungry and never got enough to eat. He also said that when he asked for food, his foster mother would slap him in the face. This provided the basis for his removal and placement in a fourth home where he is now residing. Because of his troubled and turbulent background, I just want to warn you that he may have problems down the road. From what I've been able to determine from the research I've done, his three siblings have already been adopted, so he is the last one left in the system.'

"Our face-to-face visit with TJ came nine days after we had met with Mr. McIntosh. Dave had flown in from Baltimore on Thursday instead of Friday so we could pick up TJ and spend three hours with him, which was the time allotted for his first outing. Our plans were to pick him up from the agency, take him and our daughter to a park to let them run around and play for a little bit, and get to know each other.

"Later, we would stop for hot dogs or hamburgers and french fries. We would top it off with ice cream before returning him to the agency. As we entered Mr. McIntosh's office, we were met by this little boy who rolled his eyes at us, had a scowl on his face, and clenched fists. His body language was screaming, 'Don't mess with me, or I'll knock your butt off!' For whatever reason, I knew immediately that this child had been through hell and had suffered all kinds of abuse. He was trying to protect himself the only way he knew how.

"I later shared with him when he was older that 'with that act of defiance, you crawled right up into my heart and took a permanent seat.' His little belly was distended, attesting to his malnourished state, and there were several scars visible on his body. Granted, kids are clumsy, but there was something about those scars that just didn't feel right to me.

"As Mr. McIntosh introduced us by saying, 'Terrance, this is Mr. and Mrs. Ferguson and their daughter Lynn. Can you say hello to them?' I smiled and said 'Hello Terrance' as I extended my hand to shake his. He hesitated, then looked up at me, unclenched his fists, put out his little hand to shake mine, and reluctantly gave me half of a smile.

"*Bingo!* I thought. *At least he cracked the door a little bit so we can squeeze a hand through, but I think it's going to be a long journey to get him to trust me or any of us in this family. He will find out, though, that I am tenacious and determined, and I will break through that wall he's built around himself.*

"Lynn was the first to get a huge smile from TJ when she asked him if he wanted to come and live with us, be her little brother, and have his own room and lots of toys to play with. He did not look up at her but rather looked down at the floor and nodded his head as a smile crept across his face. Then, it immediately disappeared.

"Even at his tender young age, it was obvious that he had been disappointed many times and was afraid to let himself believe something good was about to happen to him. After signing papers acknowledging that we would return him at the specified time, we left the agency office and headed to a park area between Lake Shore Drive and Lake Michigan that had swings, monkey bars, slides, and a teeter-tooter. At first, TJ was reluctant to get on any of the playground equipment, but after several tries, Lynn was able to get him on the little swing and gently push him back and forth. After a while, he was laughing and telling her to push him higher and higher.

"My heart soared as I watched this scene and prayed that this was the beginning of the end of the abuse TJ had suffered up to this point. I just knew that we could give him the home, family, and support he needed to grow up and lead a vibrant, healthy, and productive life.

"Ten days later, Dave and I signed legal papers making TJ our very own son. If we had hoped for smooth sailing once we had finalized the adoption, we were in for a big surprise. For our first meal together as a family, I said to TJ, 'What do you usually like to eat?'

"He looked at me sullenly and answered, 'None 'o your business!'

"Refusing to let his response deter me, I again said, 'TJ, I want to fix your favorite food for our first meal together as a family, so what do you want me to cook?'

"'Nothing, 'cause all you gonna do is snatch it away from me when I start to eat it.'

"Turning so that he could not see the tears welling in my eyes, I waited for a minute, then said, 'TJ, I'm going to cook some fried chicken, macaroni and cheese, and we're going to have apple pie with ice cream for dessert. I promise. Look at me, TJ,' I said as I turned his little face toward me and made the sign of the cross over my heart. 'I cross my heart that I will not snatch it away from you. I also promise that I'm going to let you eat until you are full, okay?' As I smiled and rubbed my tummy. With that, I got a snaggletooth grin.

"Once dinner was prepared, I called everyone to the table to eat. I explained to TJ that our family always says grace or blessings to God for giving us food. I showed him how to put his hands together and told him to bow his head and close his eyes. Dave then said a short blessing. When he finished the blessing and we all opened our eyes, TJ had taken over half the chicken off the platter and piled it on his plate, and his mouth was so full that I was afraid he would choke. Recovering from his shock, Dave explained to him that he should only take one or two pieces at one time.

"As he reached over to take the other pieces and put them back on the platter, TJ grabbed his fork, pointed the tines at Dave, and said even with his mouth still half-full of chicken, 'If you take my chicken, I'll beat your butt!'

"Dave immediately responded, 'No, you're not going to beat my butt, TJ, and you don't have to beat anybody's butt to get food. You can have as much as you want, but you will not pile all the food on your plate when your mother cooked that food for all of us.' Dave asked him what other pieces he liked, then left two legs and a thigh on his plate and returned the rest to the platter.

"We recognized early on that TJ was manifesting characteristics of destructive behavior. Before bringing him home, we bought him several stuffed toys that he could snuggle with when he went to sleep. In less than a week, every single stuffed toy had been completely destroyed. We found the blue teddy bear's leg under his bed, the raccoon's tail behind the couch in the family room, the brown teddy bear's two plastic eyes and red felt mouth in the bathroom trash. Mounds of stuffing here and there confirmed the demise of the stuffed animals.

"TJ's nightmares were constant, and many times, he would wake up screaming, 'Don't hit me!' or 'I didn't steal no hot dogs.' At first, I was confused by the hot dog statement until I remembered Mr. McIntosh telling us about the incident where TJ had been so hungry that he ate the package of frozen hot dogs. Lord only knows how much he was beaten for that.

"I also noticed that TJ was becoming more and more defiant. I would ask him to do something, and he would either say, 'No,' stick out his bottom lip, roll his eyes, fold his arms across his chest, and just stand there and refuse to move. At first, I was wrestling with how to be firm without causing him to reject us even more. The first couple of times it happened, I just walked away and let it go. After giving it some thought, though, I realized I was doing more harm than good while creating a little monster in the process. So, the next time that happened, I went over to him, knelt down, put my arms around him, gave him a hug, and told him I knew exactly what he was trying to do.

"'TJ, I know you are trying to make me angry enough so that I will either hit you or not love you anymore. That is not going to happen! I may not like it that you refuse to do what I ask you to do, but I love you and will continue to love you no matter what. Your being stubborn will not make me stop loving you. Now, little man, get your butt moving and go over there and do what I told you to do ten minutes ago.' He gave me his sly little grin and trotted off to do his task.

"Once Dave and I had made the decision to adopt, we began construction on a new home in Downers Grove, Illinois, a suburb located about twenty miles west of downtown Chicago. We also knew that Muh Dear, who I now simply called Mother, was eighty-seven years old and would soon be unable to live alone. We had only been living there a couple of months before bringing TJ home.

"Within two weeks after the adoption, our home went from having a brand-new carpet smell to that of a well-used outhouse or a latrine. During the first couple of days, we learned that TJ had a bed-wetting problem, and so I was fine with stripping his bed and washing him up every morning as I was getting him dressed for the day.

"At first, we were trying to figure out why the urine smell was permeating the entire house, even though I was constantly washing his sheets and pajamas. Walking through the door, the smell was almost overwhelming. A few days later, I went into the living room to put flowers on the coffee table, and the urine smell was so strong I almost gagged. As I looked down at our brand-new carpet in the corner, there was a big yellow stain. Inspection of corners in the dining room and family room showed similar yellow stains and reeked of urine."

"Nanna," I interjected, *"Why do you think Dad was peeing in every corner of your new house?"*

"I really don't know, Michael, but I think he was doing everything humanly possible to get us to reject him. I don't believe that he had ever been happy or put in a place where he felt loved and wanted. Even at his young age and considering the fact that he had no idea what self-fulfilling prophesy was, that's exactly what he was trying to bring about. If he could just do enough to provoke us into hitting, abusing, or rejecting him, then he would have proven that he was unworthy to feel good or be loved. I know it's hard to believe, especially when we're talking about a little three-and-a-half-year-old, but I recognized early on that your dad was one smart and intuitive little boy.

"Getting back to the story, I found an excellent carpet

cleaning service that we hired to come in and try to work their magic with removing the stains and the smell. Little did I know that during the first eighteen months of the time we lived in that house, they would have to do three repeat performances. I think we finally accepted the fact that our house would never again regain that new carpet smell.

"TJ was a child of few words. His familiar responses of 'I don't know' and 'I didn't do it,' along with that 'I am innocent' puppy-dog stare belied the fact that his little mind was constantly churning and bringing more devious and destructive acts to the surface. For a child as young as TJ, he understood well the old adage, 'If at first you don't succeed, try, try again.'

"The first couple of months following TJ's adoption, I was able to stay home with him since school was out for the summer. I tried to use that time to get to know him better, and as a family, we planned and went on several weekend trips that we hoped he would enjoy. During that summer, we thought we were making progress. TJ began laughing more, playing with Lynn and his cousins who came to visit from Michigan, learning how to play tee-ball, learning how to swim, and going to amusement parks. For a brief period, we were confident we were headed toward reaching our goal of getting him settled in and moving him past his acting out and exhibiting bizarre behavior phase.

"However, once September rolled around, we had to place him in a daycare program. After doing several weeks of research and leg work, we felt the program at Woodview Daycare Center in Maywood would be perfect. It had been highly recommended by a couple of friends whose children attended there. It was also located right off the freeway where I traveled to get to the Lawndale section of Chicago.

"TJ had only been enrolled in the school about two weeks when I started receiving the calls. First, it was him beating up the other little kids and taking their toys. Next, he was caught stealing cookies out of the pantry cabinet. Then, he started bullying the other children and taking their food during snack time. He even destroyed a couple of books by tearing pages out and coloring them. They later found that once he had finished coloring, he had broken all twenty-four crayons and hid them under the book shelf. We were kindly asked to replace the books and the box of crayons.

"I will always be grateful to the staff of Woodview because they hung in there with TJ for two years in spite of all the disruption he caused and the challenges they faced in dealing with him. I was so proud of him the day he graduated and thought my chest would burst. He was adorable and picture-perfect as he marched in with the other children in his white cap and gown. At that moment, I silently prayed that this scene would be repeated in twelve years. Little did I know that the challenges we would face between June 1978 and June 1990 would be like climbing Mt. Everest with little or no training in mountain climbing and while suffering with asthma.

"Realizing that TJ had made it through Woodview by the skin of his teeth, we knew that other schools would not be so forgiving. This proved to be true as TJ entered the Downers Grove public school system the following fall. For the next three years as he moved through the primary grades at Grove Elementary School, we were constantly receiving calls or being asked to attend parent-teacher or parent-administrator meetings to deal with problems regarding his disruptive and destructive behavior.

"We also came to realize that neither Dave nor I was equipped to deal with TJ's problems. Both teachers and administrators suggested we get some professional help with what appeared to be a mountain of emotional and psychological issues. After asking around to see if anyone we knew could recommend a child psychologist and having no luck, I began looking in the yellow pages. I came across Dr. Symone O'Chians, a child psychologist affiliated with the University of Chicago.

"As I read her ad, it sounded like she might be a good fit for TJ since she had been in business for eighteen years, had experience in working with difficult cases, and had endorsements from several highly respected sources. I immediately contacted her office and arranged for a phone conference. She called me later that afternoon, and after giving her a brief overview, we set up an appointment for Thursday the following week. However, we never got the opportunity to keep that appointment."

TWELVE

Transition

"On Friday when Dave flew home from California, he informed us that he had just been promoted to become west coast regional superintendent and that we would be moving to California in a month. 'What! Are you serious?' I asked. The following Monday, we were all on a plane headed for California, hoping to find a home located in a neighborhood with good schools. That was our top priority. We had the option of Dave and me going by ourselves or taking Lynn and TJ with us. We chose the latter, thinking this would make the transition easier, especially for TJ since his life up to this point had been filled with constant moves and instability. We were also hoping that a trip to Disneyland would get him excited about moving to a place that had an amusement park like Disneyland.

"The trip turned out as we had hoped, for the most part. After enduring Chicago winters year after year, California was enticing with its constant sunshine, warm weather, beautiful palm trees, mountains, and beaches. For our first meal, we stopped at a restaurant that had an atrium in the middle, and we could hardly eat our food for staring at the beautiful flowers and trees. Lynn showed a real appetite for seafood, and as usual, TJ couldn't get enough hamburgers and french fries. We found a couple of houses we liked in great neighborhoods that had schools with impressive track records, but the asking prices were quite steep. Acting on a hunch, I asked the realtor who was showing us different properties if she had any listings of foreclosures. She immediately perked up and said, 'Why, yes, there is one off Colima Road in Hacienda Heights that just came on the market. Would you like to see it?'

"'Of course,' I interjected, hoping that we could find a bargain and something we could afford somewhere in Southern California.

"From the minute we drove up to the property and parked in the driveway, it was obvious that it had been grossly neglected. The front yard was completely brown; not even one sprig of green grass could be seen anywhere on the lawn. Several bushes were also dead, and the few that remained looked like they were on their last leg. As we entered the house, the putrid smell was almost unbearable. 'Good grief, this place stinks!' Dave said without giving any thought to how the realtor would react.

"'Yes it does,' she agreed, 'but the place has real potential structurally, and location-wise, it's a steal. Don't be misled by appearances because that is cosmetic, and you would be surprised at the difference a good cleaning and painting could make. Once you get this soiled carpet and drapes out of here, the place will smell much better too.'

"We later learned that, prior to foreclosure, the house had been occupied by three families living together to try and make ends meet. From the looks of it, though, no one had given a thought to turning on the sprinklers to help the front lawn survive the heat. The house reeked of garlic, grease, dog urine and feces, molded carpet, and who knows what else. The dismal condition was further exacerbated by the condition of the Olympic-sized swimming pool with cracks so large it appeared to have gone through a major earthquake. The pool contained so much algae that it looked like a sea of green, the color the front lawn should have been.

"In spite of it all, the house was 2,800-square-feet of possibilities. The downstairs consisted of a formal living room with a soaring cathedral ceiling, a separate formal dining room with its own patio, a kitchen, family room with a fireplace and dining area, and a bedroom with a bath which would be perfect for Mother. As we ventured upstairs, I really began to get excited. The transom windows that were placed above the front door were the exact height as the hallway outside the master bedroom. From that vantage point, one could look out and see the breathtaking view of the snow-capped San Bernardino Mountains.

"The master bedroom was humongous and had two large closets, a bathroom, and a wall of windows overlooking the backyard and pool. There were two other large-size bedrooms on the upper level, which would be perfect for TJ and Lynn. The real draw, though, was what the realtor referred to as a bonus room. This room was unusually bright with a beamed cathedral ceiling and two large triangular-shaped transom windows set high in the wall that followed the shape of the ceiling. The design offered both light and privacy. The room ran almost the entire width of the house and was large enough to easily accommodate fifty people. It could be the perfect playroom and, as the kids got older, a game or TV room where they could entertain their friends.

"Taking into consideration that the house was located in a great neighborhood with excellent schools and close proximity to parks and shopping, the pros seemed to outweigh the cons. After a brief discussion, Dave and I made an offer on the house, and it was accepted.

"While Dave and the kids returned to Chicago, I flew to Little Rock to inform Mother that we would be bringing her to California with us. During the long flight there, I had time to reflect on what had transpired with Mother over the past fifteen years following Daddy's death in 1967. After the funeral, Mother had insisted on staying in Little Rock by herself rather than move to Michigan where Dave and I lived prior to Chicago. She said she did not want to leave her house, neighbors, friends, or her church. I made certain I went down to see her at least three or four times a year.

"At first, she seemed to be doing well as she continued singing in the church choir and attending and sometimes teaching her weekly Bible study sessions. She did curtail her involvement with some of the organizations she had been affiliated with when I was growing up but continued with the Eastern Star, the NAACP, and the National Council of Negro Women. Still, her favorite activity was meeting other women down at the church and helping prepare and deliver meals to the sick and shut-ins. However, as the years passed and Mother's health began to deteriorate, I knew it was only a matter of time before we would have to bring her to live with us.

"During the years following Daddy's death, Dave finished school in Michigan and got a job in the elevator industry whereby we moved to Chicago. There, I began teaching high school music on Chicago's west side and started conducting high school and church choral groups. Four years after I began teaching, I decided to return to college and get a Master of Music degree from Northwestern University in Evanston.

"For years, I had been interested in the status of the music program in the Chicago Public Schools; therefore, I conducted extensive research and interviews as a basis for my thesis project. I was hoping to get prepared to eventually apply for an administrative position in music, if and when one became available. Little did I know then that becoming an administrator was not in my future.

"Once I finished graduate school and resumed working, that's when Dave and I began making plans to build a home to accommodate the child we were planning to adopt and Mother. We searched and found a location, purchased the land, selected a model, and began working with the architect to redesign the second level where Mother would be living.

"We had him add additional footage to her bedroom to accommodate a queen-size or hospital bed if her care ever required it and added more lighting because of her poor eyesight. He also redesigned the bathroom to include more space, a higher toilet, handrails, an easy-access tub and shower, and an emergency call button. Both her bedroom and bathroom had intercom systems in case she needed to contact us or vice versa on one of the other three levels. All doors were widened for easy wheelchair access. Her level also contained a large family room and dining area which allowed her to eat, watch TV, and interact with the rest of the family without having to climb stairs.

"Seven months after we finished building our home, I started getting calls from Mother's neighbors, tenant, and others concerned about her well-being. On several different occasions, they called to inform me of numerous incidents that appeared to be telltale signs that she was dealing with dementia. Mother got lost one day right in front of her house and continued to drive around the same block for almost an hour. A neighbor, sitting on the front porch, realized what was happening and ran out to the street and flagged her down to stop her. The janitor at her church called and said she showed up with her choir robe for Sunday morning service on a Wednesday morning and could not understand why no one else was there for service.

"The owner of the little neighborhood market where Mother had shopped for years called to inform me that she had shown up to buy groceries wearing a nightgown, her hat, and gloves. The scariest of all, though, was when her tenant, Miss Ola Mae, who had rented a room from Mother for over twenty years, called to tell me that Mother had started a small fire in the stove. Apparently, when she was trying to broil a steak, she put the oven mitt in the stove along with the pan of steak she was cooking.

"Within a week after the call from Miss Ola Mae, Dave and I were in Little Rock preparing to bring her back to Illinois. It was obvious now that Mother could no longer live alone or care for herself. Her doctor confirmed to us that she was in the early stages of dementia. It was difficult to come to the realization that Mother was no longer the person I had known all my life. I could only remember her being strong, wise, tenacious, mentally sharp, healthy, competent, energetic, and always, always in charge. My first reaction was to cry uncontrollably and come up with all kinds of excuses for her bizarre actions, which only showed I was in complete denial. How could someone who had saved my life, taught me right from wrong, and who was responsible for making me the person I had become now be dealing with such a devastating illness?"

"Trying to convince Mother that she needed to move to Downers Grove and live with us was no easy task. She fought us every step of the way and was adamant about not selling her home and furniture, which we could understand. She even resorted to sitting in one of the chairs to prevent the man from loading it onto his truck, even though he had purchased it, and she was holding his payment in her hands. Mother even began saying that Dave and I were 'treating her like a dog,' which only added to the heartbreak we were feeling about the whole situation.

"Never in my wildest dream would I have imagined that our mother-daughter roles would reverse, and I would be the one making the crucial decisions about her future, health, and safety. And so, it was that in August of 1978, Mother arrived in Downers Grove, Illinois, to live with us. Little did we know then that thirteen months later, we would be back to square one with her.

"Mother had been discontent from the minute she walked into our house, and things only went downhill from there.

Surprisingly, though, she loved TJ and Lynn and would sit in the family room for hours telling them about her childhood. Often, she would repeat the same stories over and over again, but they didn't seem to mind. She also had a special way of getting TJ to be on his better, not 'best,' but better behavior than what he displayed when he was not around Mother. I can still remember her chastising him, as she would say, 'TJ, why you want to act so ugly like that? Baby, you know you're not supposed to act like that!' And for a brief moment, he would straighten up and fly right to appease her.

"Unfortunately, there seemed to be nothing we could do to make her happy or encourage her to settle in and enjoy not having to worry about or want for anything. With the onset of winter, things only got worse, and she would constantly complain that living in Illinois was like always living in an icebox. We tried to address that concern by getting a couple of space heaters for her bedroom and the family room to make her living space more cozy and comfortable. However, much to our surprise, shock, and dismay, we came home on September 15, 1979, after work to find her gone.

"We were frantic and on the verge of calling the police to report her missing when we received a call from one of our neighbors who had seen her leaving with her luggage and had run out to find out where she was going. Mother informed her that she was on her way back to Little Rock to take care of some personal business. Yep, she had just up and left.

"There is no way of knowing how long she had been planning her get-away, but she was smart enough, even with her dementia, to wait until after summer vacation was over. She knew that in September, I would be back to work, and the kids would be back in school, so no one would be there to see her leave. Unbeknownst to us, she had contacted one of the men from her church and had him come pick her up and take her to the bus station where she headed back to Little Rock on her own. I was beside myself with worry. How could I not have seen it coming?"

"Nanna, you mean she just packed up and left after every-thing you and Grandpa had done? You even redesigned the house to make it more comfortable for her, right?"

"Yes, she did! But it's not about the expense we had incurred. It was totally about her safety and well-being. I must admit, though, that this was such a crushing blow, and I was devastated.

"The second day after we discovered her missing, I received a call from one of Mother's neighbors, Ms. Bernice Watson. She had just picked her up from the bus station and said that Mother had asked if she could live with her because she didn't want to live up north in that icebox ever again. Ms. Watson said she would be willing to rent Mother a room and that she would look after her and take good care of her. My immediate thought was to get on a plane, fly to Little Rock, have a good talk with Mother, and see for myself where she would be staying. However, Ms. Watson assured me that I didn't need to do that.

"Since I had known her all while I was growing up, I felt that she would do exactly as she said. However, in the back of my mind, there was this nagging thought that since Ms. Watson was around Mother's age, she might be suffering some dementia or similar problems of her own. If that was the case, then would she be able to take care of herself and Mother too?

Yet, against my better judgement, I acquiesced. I figured I would be flying down in three months anyway to spend Christmas with Mother, so I could check on her then and see how well she was faring.

"Unfortunately, my plan was thwarted when I became quite ill in early December and was in bed during most of the Christmas break. Not wanting to risk getting Mother sick, I resorted to sending her gifts and calling her on Christmas Day.

"Little did I know at that time that the 'room' Ms. Watson had agreed to rent to Mother had originally been a screened-in back porch and that she had simply replaced the screening with some sheets of drywall with no insulation whatsoever. As a result, the place was scorching hot in the summer and unbearably cold in the winter. About four months after Mother moved in with her, and now it was January and the dead of winter, I received a call from the emergency room at Baptist Hospital.

"They informed me that Mother was being admitted, was seriously ill, and that I should get there as soon as possible. By 10:10 the next morning, I was walking into her hospital room. My heart was in my mouth as I saw her with tubes running everywhere and witnessed her struggling to catch every breath. Soon after my arrival, the doctor came in and explained the seriousness of her condition. Mother had pneumonia, was suffering from dehydration, and had congestive heart failure. He was adamant about her needing to be placed in an environment where she would have decent living conditions, could receive proper health care, and prevent worsening of her condition.

"Mother had made it quite clear that she was never going

back to Downers Grove or anywhere else where she would be forced to live in a place so cold that it was like living in a refrigerator, or to use her term, an icebox. We still had a few relatives living in Arkansas, but none of them were in a position to care for her. Therefore, I began looking for a reputable nursing home. After calling and visiting numerous homes, I finally settled on one located just outside Little Rock's city limits and only a fifteen-minute drive from Scott, where it had all begun forty years before. Five days after arriving and with a heart so heavy it felt like a ship's anchor, I checked Mother into Gilliam's Nursing Home.

"For twenty-eight months, I had made the twenty-plus-hours roundtrip drive from Downers Grove to Little Rock at least every six weeks. The routine became an easy one to follow. Thursday nights before the trip, the kids and I would lay out what we were taking and pack the car. Since Dave was traveling for work most of the time, he seldom made the trip with us. On Fridays after work, I would grab the kids from school around 3:30, head to Interstate 57 South toward Memphis, pick up Interstate 55 South about six hours later, and continue about another hour and forty-five minutes before hitting Interstate 40 just outside of Memphis around one in the morning.

"This was always encouraging since I knew I was just a little over an hour and thirty minutes away from my destination and would put us in Little Rock somewhere around 3:00 a.m. Most times, we would head straight for Gilliam's Nursing Home, pull into their parking lot, sleep until around eight, then go inside to have breakfast with Mother.

"To make better time than if I simply drove the speed

limit, I would rely on TJ and Lynn to keep vigilance by monitoring the front and back windows for the highway patrol. I also relied on my CB trucker friends who knew me by my handle because I traveled that route so much."

"Whoa, Nanna," I interrupted, "What's a CB, and what kind of handle are you talking about?"

"Oh, sorry, Michael, I guess you wouldn't know what a CB is. CB is a slang term for Citizens Band radio. Back in the 1970s and early 1980s, CBs were used to communicate with other people who were tuned in to the same frequency. In order for others to recognize who they were talking to, CB users would adopt a name known as their 'handle.' My handle was 'Porschebear 38' since I loved the Porsche and hoped that one day, I would be able to own one. The 38 was my age at the time. Most of the CB users were truckers who were out on the road all the time.

"This was a great way for them to communicate with other truckers, find out about accidents or road conditions ahead, and send alerts of smokey or highway patrol locations so they could adjust their speed accordingly. Dave had suggested I get one since I was traveling back and forth between Downers Grove and Little Rock so much. Of course, these were the days long before cell phones.

"Anyway, getting back to my story, the truckers would always alert me to smokey's location so I could slow down if necessary. I traveled that route so much that I began to run into the same truckers each time I made the trip. I particularly remember one instance when I was flying down I-40 around two in the morning and was so focused on getting to the nursing home to see about Mother that I was not paying attention to my speed.

"All of a sudden, there were flashing lights in my rearview mirror. Just at that moment, one of my trucker friends who I had been talking to earlier came on the CB and told me to quickly pull over into the right lane in front of him. I did as I was told, and just as I made it to the right lane, the big eighteen-wheeler that had been traveling in the left lane in front of me slowed down.

"At the same time, the truck in the right lane closed in behind me, preventing the highway patrol car from getting into the right lane behind me. Both trucks paced me for about half a mile when one of the truckers told me to get off at the next exit. I did so, and by the truckers blocking the highway patrol's vision, when he realized I had taken the exit, he had passed the exit ramp, and I was safe. Whew! From there on, I watched my speed.

"I was determined to demonstrate to Mother that we had not abandoned her and that I loved her as much as anyone could possibly love another human being. Even though I had carefully selected the home where she was presently residing, I liked showing up unannounced to see if she was getting the proper care.

"A surprise visit during the sixteenth month she was there was quite disturbing. I had made my usual visit two weeks before, and Mother's roommate had mentioned that the nursing staff had figured out about the time I was coming to visit her. So, they would ignore Mother's request and complaints and keep her sedated until it was close to the time they knew I would be returning for a visit. She even mentioned that sometimes they would leave Mother sitting in her chair nodding and trying to get comfortable long after she should have been put to bed. Much of it sounded factual because Mother was starting to look more and more fragile.

"So, instead of waiting the usual six weeks, I got a friend to watch the kids, took a flight to Little Rock two weeks later, and showed up at the nursing home on a Wednesday around noon. When I walked in, the shock on their faces showed they were visibly shaken. Even before I got to Mother's room, I knew that much of what her roommate had told me had just been confirmed. Without saying a word, I headed straight for her room. One of the nurses was running along beside me saying something about Mother not feeling well, and so they had let her sleep in.

"On the contrary, when I walked in, Mother was struggling to try to sit up and complaining about how hungry she was. When I went over to her bed, she immediately recognized me and said, 'Baby, I've been calling these folks all morning trying to get something to eat, and my bed is wet, too, because nobody came to help me get to the bathroom. They just act like they don't hear me, and I know they do.'

"There was a half-empty tray of food on her roommate's table but nothing on Mother's. It was also clear that they had not taken care of her hygiene needs either. No wonder she looked so thin and frail the last time I had visited.

"Needless to say, I stormed out of her room, demanded a meeting immediately with the nursing staff, and 'held court.' I did not mince words, and to this day remember saying, 'If I every show up again and find my mother in the deplorable condition she is now, all of you will be sorry you ever laid eyes on me or my mother.

"'Hear me clearly! I will have this place closed down so fast you won't know what hit you. That lady in there who you are mistreating is precious to me! She is my mother! She is my diamond, my gem, and I will not stand around and let you treat her like she is a piece of garbage. Right now, she looks like she hasn't had a proper meal in days, and when was the last time you gave her a bath or shower?

"'I am paying you good money to take good care of her, and I expect nothing less. My promise to her is to get her out of this retched place as soon as I can. In the meantime, though, I expect her to be treated the way she deserves to be treated: with respect, compassion, and good quality care. Have I made myself clear? For your sake, I certainly hope so. Now, please, go in there, clean my mother up, and bring some food so I can have the pleasure of feeding her.'

"During that visit, I also learned that Mother was on seventeen different medications which made her lethargic, so much so that she just slept a great deal of the time. Even though she had been happy to see me, her eyes seem lifeless, and the twinkle that was so much a part of her was gone. She was definitely fighting depression.

"It was also evident that she was getting very little exercise. When I took her out for lunch and her favorite Dairy Queen treat the following day, she could barely walk, even with the help of her cane. I think that trip was the most emotional one I made during the entire time she was there. Before leaving, I promised Mother that I was going to get her out of that nursing home and back living with us again. When I had made that promise, I had no idea how I was going to accomplish that feat since I knew she would never return to Illinois.

"That had taken place about a year ago. Now, the answer had come with Dave receiving his transfer to California, and I couldn't wait to share the good news with her. When I arrived at the nursing home and began sharing with Mother, she seemed confused when I told her that we were going to be living together again, but this time, it would be California where it was sunny and warm. At first, she didn't quite make the connection but smiled and clapped her hands when I told her that she was going to be able to tell her childhood stories to TJ and Lynn again anytime she wanted to.

"I also added a little icing on the cake by mentioning that she would be able to have Dairy Queen every day if she wished. I ended my visit to the home by informing the staff that she would be moving to California in three weeks. I left Little Rock with joy in my heart again."

THIRTEEN

California, Here We Come

"Early on Saturday morning, June 12, 1982, we said goodbye to our home in Downers Grove and headed toward Interstate 55 on our way to southern California via Little Rock, Arkansas. So, here we were in our little gold colored 1981 Audi 5000, Dave, Lynn, TJ, our dog, Ebony, and me heading to Little Rock to pick up Mother. No sooner had we hit Interstate 57 South when Lynn began making up a song to the tune of 'California, Here We Come.' Five minutes later, she had the words down pat and began teaching them to us."

California here we come
Daddy, TJ, Lynn and Mom;
From Illi, to Cali
We're on our way.

Thru Texi, New Mexi, Oklahoma, Arizona,
We will pick up Grandma too,
Mom said nothing else will do,
Look out folks we're coming thru,
California here we come.

"The drive was a nostalgic one. As I watched the passing scenery, I recalled the many times I had traveled this route over the past twenty-eight months to visit Mother. This time was different, though, for it would be the last time I would be making this trip. No longer would I have to worry about how she was being cared for since we were going to be her care-takers now. Just to be able to spend time with her again on a daily basis was a dream come true. I could hardly wait.

"Ten hours later, our little packed Audi pulled into the parking lot of Gilliam's Nursing Home. The staff had made sure Mother was all packed up and ready to go. Because of her fragile state, she was now in a wheelchair. They had her all decked out in her hat, which she always wore whenever she was going outdoors or any place else. She waved goodbye to the other residents as one of the nurses wheeled her out to the parking lot and helped her into the car. We wanted her to be as comfortable as possible during the long drive, so Mother took my spot up front with Dave, and I sat in back with the kids and the dog.

"Mother was quite reticent as we traveled through many of the small farm towns in Arkansas she used to visit on a regular basis in her younger days. It wasn't until we had crossed over into Oklahoma that she began to interact with us. We had told the kids about her dementia problem and asked them just to observe and take their cues from her before trying to get her to talk or play games with them. As the trip progressed, her mood seemed to lighten up, and she actually started laughing and teasing with the kids. Because of the cramped space in the car, we stopped often to stretch our legs.

"On one of those stops, we spotted a Dairy Queen and treated Mother to her favorite peanut buster parfait. I handed it to her, and as she began eating, she gave me the biggest smile I had seen in months. When she finally emptied her mouth enough to speak, she said, 'Baby, this sure is some good ice cream. I could eat this ice cream all day long.' That was music to my ears. However, lingering in the back of my mind was the question, 'Will she be happy in California, or will she be so unhappy that she'll take off, or at least try to take off again?'

"Around Six in the evening on Tuesday, June 15th, three days after we had left our home in Downers Gove, we pulled into the parking lot of Mid-Town Motel in Rowland Heights, California. The drive had been long, hot, and tiring. Sitting in such a close and cramped space for three days made the trip even more exhausting, especially with five people and a dog in our little car. Yet we were happy to finally be in southern California. We were definitely looking forward to starting a new life and embracing new opportunities here.

"Dave and I decided we did not want Mother and the kids exposed to the germs we knew were lurking at the new house, so we decided to leave them at the motel. The next day, we got up early, swung by the realtor's office to pick up the keys, and headed to the new house to start cleaning and preparing it for our furniture, which would be arriving in a few days.

"We pulled up to the house, walked past the brown lawn that seemed even more dried out than it was a month ago, put the key in the front lock, opened the door, and nearly passed out. What on earth were we thinking when we bought this heap of mess? The smell, dirt, and assault on our senses hit us like a ton of bricks. How on earth were we ever going to get this place habitable again? Without a doubt, it was going to be a Herculean task.

"For the next several days, Dave and I worked to the point of complete exhaustion, dragging out garbage, debris, and two dead rats we found under the stove. We scraped about an inch of accumulated grease and gook off the kitchen floor, stove, cabinets, and kitchen fixtures.

"Washing and disinfecting the walls presented one of the biggest challenges since the living room and foyer had walls twenty-two-feet-high, and I was petrified of climbing the ladder to try and scrub them. As we continued to plow through the muck and the mire, I had to keep reminding myself that in disguise, this house was really a blessing. Had it not been in foreclosure, we could never have afforded such a house in California.

"Two weeks after we arrived, we moved out of the motel and into our new home. What a transformation! The kids, who had not seen it since our initial visit over a month ago, could not believe their eyes. They were greeted by newly painted walls after we finally realized they were past the point of coming clean with scrubbing. The newly laid carpet throughout the entire house brightened up the place and brought a new smell which was sorely needed. The parquet floors in the foyer and the kitchen gleamed like they were brand new. Sparkling new light fixtures and chandeliers in the foyer and dining room gave the house a totally different look. TJ said he could not wait to jump into our newly cleaned and resurfaced swimming pool.

"Mother couldn't wait to see her room, and even though it was not as spacious or as well-equipped as the one in Downers Grove, it was still a beautiful room. She had two large windows that offered lots of light and a view of the pool and the fruit trees that surrounded the entire backyard area of the house.

"In spite of all the great things that we were experiencing, our biggest concern was still TJ. Would he adjust to being uprooted yet again and transported over 2,000 miles from where he had spent his entire life up to this point? We had made certain both he and Lynn had bedrooms that we decorated to reflect their ages, personalities, and interests. We left the bonus room for the kids to decorate any way they liked and told them they would be allowed to select the furnishings. We hoped this would be enough, but only time would tell.

"Once we settled in, it was time for me to look for a job, get the kids registered for school, find a church, and check out all that California had to offer. I had fallen in love with teaching high school and wanted desperately to find another high school choral music position. I soon found out, though, that southern California was different from Chicago, and high school choral music positions were as scarce as hen's teeth. September rolled around, and no job was forthcoming, even though I had applied in eight or nine districts. So, I signed up to do substitute teaching.

"Meanwhile, TJ's problems were becoming more evident as he began displaying more and more bizarre behavior. At first, there were small incidents like running away from home and spending the day down at the mall, which was located two and a half blocks away. About a month after we moved into our new home, TJ had been riding his bike through the neighborhood when he spotted one of our neighbor's cars parked in their driveway with the windows rolled down. He snuck up to the car and stole the garage door opener that was clipped to the sun visor, brought it home, and hid it in his room.

"On Tuesday of the following week around mid-day, he asked if he could go to the park near the house to play with some of his new friends. I immediately said yes, happy that he was getting adjusted and meeting new people.

"Little did I know that once he left the house, he headed to the home where he had stolen the opener. Seeing that the car was gone, he figured the occupants were at work. He opened the garage door, went into their home, turned on the TV, raided their refrigerator, made himself at home, and apparently fell asleep.

"He was abruptly awakened when he heard the garage door opening. Panicking, he tried to run out the front door but needed a key to unlock it. He turned around, ran out the door leading into the garage, and past the lady who was attempting to get groceries out of her car. Figuring he could get away faster if he had a set of wheels, he grabbed a bike that was sitting right by the garage door entrance and took off down the street. Not being familiar with riding a bike that large and not being able to control it as he raced down the hill, he ended up crashing into the brick wall surrounding the church parking lot across the street from our house.

"The cost of replacing the new $300 Schwinn bike was just the beginning of numerous replacement expenses we would incur over the next seven years. Because the neighbor had reported the incident to the Puente Hills Police Department, that was the beginning of TJ's police record.

"Before we could recover from that incident, less than one week later, we received a phone call from the police department again, stating that they had our son in custody and that we needed to come down to the station immediately. 'Oh my Lord, what has TJ done now, and why is he all the way down at the police station?' was my immediate response. Again, he was supposed to be playing at the park with some of his new friends.

"I walked in, and there was TJ sitting in a chair staring at his feet. The officer immediately began to explain what happened. Apparently, TJ had gone to the mall but didn't have any money. So, when he got hungry, he went into J.C. Penney's and grabbed several bags of candy that were sitting on a rack in front of the candy counter and tried to run away. However, a store employee was able to trip him as he ran by and took him to their office where they called the police.

"The officer commented that he was concerned since this was the second incident in less than a week. He also stated that he knew TJ was from a good home with caring parents because he was very polite when they spoke to him and asked him questions. Meanwhile, I'm thinking to myself, *So, you're giving him Brownie points for being a polite thief, huh?* In my book, a thief is a thief!

"I know this is not an excuse, but with all the focus on the move, picking up Mother, and getting all of us settled in, looking for a child psychologist had been pushed to the back burner. Now, reality was hitting, and I realized I had to get TJ some professional help immediately.

"Before I could begin searching, though, I received a call from someone connected with the police department stating that our family had been referred to him because of suspected psychological problems with our son. After a lengthy conversation, I set up an appointment for Dave, TJ, and me to meet with Dr. Sheldon the following week.

"Our visit with Dr. Sheldon lasted almost two hours. We began with a joint session where we all just shared general information. Later when he met with Dave and me separately, we shared that TJ's mother used drugs while she was pregnant with him; the thirty-nine months he had spent in foster care; the abuse he endured during those thirty-nine months; and the escalation of his bizarre behavior since adoption.

"Finally, he took TJ into a different room, talked to him, and administered some assessment tests. During this time, Dr. Sheldon determined that TJ needed to be admitted to a facility where he could be observed extensively over an extended period of time to determine how best to address his emotional and psychological needs. Since Dr. Sheldon was affiliated with Fitzgerald Medical Center, he recommended that TJ be admitted to that facility.

"Dave and I came home from our initial meeting with Dr. Sheldon and discussed at length the projected cost of TJ's hospital stay. We knew it would be expensive, and because I was only working as a substitute teacher, the entire burden would fall on his insurance. Coming to the conclusion, though, that we didn't have much of a choice, we gave Dr. Sheldon the go-ahead to get TJ admitted. On September 8, 1982, he entered Fitzgerald Hospital for psychological evaluation.

"During the six months TJ was in the hospital, we were required to attend bi-monthly family meetings with TJ's team of doctors, supervisors, and therapists. I also made sure that at least one of us made the weekly trip to visit him. The last thing I wanted to happen was to have TJ think we had abandoned him, which would simply reinforce the negative experiences and the feelings of abandonment he had had in the foster homes.

"Doctors and therapists would give us occasional updates and reassure us that they were making progress with TJ. Their main focus was addressing his impulsive and destructive behavior, teaching him how to communicate, help him to consider the consequences of his actions before acting, and making better choices.

"They explained that TJ was learning to verbally express his feelings of fear, sadness, anger, and guilt rather than 'acting them out.' The merit system they encouraged us to use once TJ was released rewarded him for good behavior and for communicating to us when he was experiencing an emotion that made him sad or feel badly.

"Almost six months to the day he entered Fitzgerald Hospital, we received a call informing us that TJ was being released the following day. Lynn and I immediately took off to the mall to get new toys, games, clothes, balloons, and material to make a banner. Our final stop was the grocery store where we bought food to prepare TJ's favorite meal as well as goodies that Lynn would put in a 'Welcome Home' basket for him. What a celebration it was going to be!

"Yes, it would be good to have TJ home again."

FOURTEEN

The Test of Faith

"The huge 'WELCOME HOME' sign hung over the entrance to the family room and was the first thing we saw as we entered the house after picking up TJ. He looked at it and gave us his little lopsided grin. My heart just soared. I silently prayed, 'Lord, let this be a new beginning for him.'

"We were so excited that he was finally home. If he had reached a point where he could function in the world sans his antics, then the cost of the program was money well spent. Now, we could look forward to a life with a lot more normalcy than we had experienced for the past six years. We hoped, especially for TJ's sake, that the demons that seemed to have plagued him were gone. Much as I hate to admit it, our euphoria was short-lived.

"Anxious to get TJ caught up on all the schoolwork he had missed while at Fitzgerald, I began looking for a school that offered year-around instruction. I located just the place—about a fifteen-minute drive from our home.

"On April 4, 1983, I enrolled TJ at Learning World, a private kindergarten through eighth grade school in Whittier. I was given permission to escort him to his classroom and meet his new teacher, Ms. Amberchrombie. After greeting us, she turned around to the class and said, 'Students, we have a new student who recently moved here from the Chicago area. Would you please say good morning to TJ?' The students all responded, 'Good morning, TJ.' Ms. Amberchrombie found a seat for TJ at a table with two other boys and told him she would get him a set of books.

"She gave me a list of things I would need to get for him by the next day and assured me that TJ would really enjoy attending Learning World. I left the campus feeling I had made a great choice, even though the tuition was pretty steep. This setting with a smaller pupil-teacher ratio was perfect for him.

"Two weeks after TJ returned home from Fitzgerald, we were celebrating Lynn's fourteenth birthday with a pool party. The kids were playing around and having loads of fun when all of a sudden TJ fell and started screaming that he had hit his head on the edge of the pool. We saw no blood or a knot on his head, so we tried to calm him down. However, he just kept screaming to the point where I panicked. I ran in and called 9-1-1 while Lynn and some of her friends kept watch and tried to keep him calm.

"The ambulance arrived in about five minutes, and as they were bringing the stretcher through the house to reach the backyard, TJ suddenly jumped up, started laughing hysterically, ran around the house, opened the gate, and took off down the street like a madman. I stood there embarrassed and in tears. What a thing to do at his sister's birthday party! Not only had he done it in front of her friends and ruined her party but had also wasted the paramedics' time and created an unnecessary expense for us for the ambulance.

"Two days after the ambulance incident, we received our first invoice from Fitzgerald for $76,824.80. My first thought was *what? There has to be some mistake! If this is no mistake, then what the heck are we paying for? TJ is acting the same if not worse than before he entered the hospital and before we spent almost $77,000!* Thank goodness that Dave's insurance offered great mental health benefits, otherwise we would have been up a creek without a paddle. At least with the insurance, we would be able to handle our portion of the bill.

"Three weeks after TJ's hospital release, we were scheduled to do a follow-up session with one of the psychiatrists who had been working with TJ. By the time we actually met with Dr. Arms, TJ had been involved in two more incidents: one at the park and another at the mall. Since Dave was traveling and unable to attend the session, Lynn and I accompanied him. We shared observations we had made of his behavior at home, and I discussed our attempts at trying to implement the merit and reward system. I said, 'Dr. Arms, we're trying everything you've recommended and more, and nothing seems to have any positive impact on his behavior whatsoever. TJ just continues to act impulsively and exhibit destructive and disruptive behavior'

"Dr. Arms said she was placing TJ on Ritalin. I immediately became alarmed because I had not heard good things about the drug. However, we were desperate for anything, and if the doctor felt it would help him, then maybe we should give it a chance. Dr. Arms also recommended that I speak to the nutritionist and get a diet guideline listing foods that would prevent over-stimulation.

"On Friday, May 27th, when I went to pick up TJ from school and to pay his tuition for the following month, I was told that Dr. Johansen, head administrator, wanted to see me in her office. Even before I entered, I knew the news was not going to be good. Dr. Johansen extended her hand, shook mine, and told me to have a seat. She then pounded the gavel down on my head as she said, 'Regretfully, TJ will no longer be able to attend Learning World due to his disruptive behavior. His behavior is hindering his teacher from giving instruction and creating an environment conducive to learning for all the students.' She continued by stating that she had 'numerous complaints from parents that he had become a major problem, and his acting out interfered with their children's ability to learn.'

"Parents also stated, 'They were not paying the kind of tuition Learning World charged to have their children subjected to the same problems children experience in public schools.' She ended our little visit by stating, 'I really hate to do this to you, Mrs. Ferguson, but we must act in the best interest of all the children. I wish you much success with finding a good school for TJ.'

"As I exited the office and headed down the hall to TJ's classroom, I couldn't help mumbling to myself, 'It certainly doesn't look like the time spent at Fitzgerald has made any difference at all.'"

"You know Nanna," I interjected, "I can't even imagine how you must have been feeling. What did you do after you picked Dad up from school?"

"Well, my first concern was Dave. What on earth was he going to say, and how would he react? That night, he and I made the decision to try to get TJ involved in some of the summer programs that Hacienda Heights had to offer. Since schools would be letting out in two weeks for summer vacation and I would be off until the beginning of September, we would have time to find some answers. It would also give us an opportunity to take some short vacations together as a family and try to help him get better adjusted and bond more with the family.

"There was no doubt that TJ was extremely talented athletically. The coaches for the summer basketball and baseball groups we signed him up for were amazed at how talented he was and how quickly he learned. The baseball coach suggested that we register him for fall football as soon as registration became available. In spite of TJ's success with the sports programs, his antics and run-ins with mall security and the Puente Hills Police Department continued to overshadow his athletic accomplishments.

"TJ was continually running away from home. One summer night in July, he slipped out of the house while I was preparing dinner and headed to the mall. Once there, he decided he was going to hang out at the arcade, make friends with some of the people who were there playing games, and hoodwink them into either paying for him to play a game or convince them to let him join in on their game. After spending a couple of hours at the arcade, he realized the mall was closing.

"Not wanting to come home and be reprimanded for running off without permission, he quickly headed to J.C. Penney's and hid under some clothes until the store closed. Once everyone was gone, he came out from his hiding place and began raiding the candy and nuts counter. Because the store had a silent alarm system embedded in the floor, he set off the alarm. The police department dispatched a couple of officers to the store, and they were able to track exactly where he was. They hauled him out of the store and brought him home since they were quite familiar with where he lived by now.

"I was so thankful that Mother was still alive and living with us and that I was able to go into her room, give her a hug, cry if I needed to, and just pour out my heart and soul to her. There was something so comforting about her presence. Even though she was suffering with dementia and at times was totally disoriented, her lucid moments were priceless. I still could not believe how much she had improved since leaving the nursing home.

"She was now down to three medications a day as opposed to the seventeen she had been on previously. She laughed and interacted more with all of us, and her appetite was voracious. Her noticeable weight gain earned her a shopping trip to the mall where she was able to pick out several new outfits. I even got to tease her about trying to pick up more than an outfit at the mall once when I left her sitting on the bench while I ran into a store to pick up a package, only to return and find her smiling and engaging in deep conversation with a man sitting on the bench with her.

"She also walked unassisted now and many times without her cane. I made sure that at least a couple of days a week, someone in the family took her for a walk around the neighborhood.

"If TJ cared for anyone, it was Mother. They seemed to have this special bond, and Mother's question to him about his behavior always elicited the same response, 'Yes, ma'am, I'm being a good boy.' Many times, I was so tempted to ask TJ, 'What is your definition of good?'

"As September approached, Dave and I realized our only option was to place him in public school. We headed to Belle Aire Elementary, the kindergarten through eighth grade school designated for students living in our neighborhood. The staff seemed quite friendly when we went to enroll him. Before school started, we made certain we had picked up all the items needed for him to get started on the right foot and have a successful school year. Back-to-school night for the parents was encouraging, and after meeting his teachers and hearing about the goals they had set for the school year, we were excited.

"Three days after school began, we received a call from the secretary at Belle Aire informing us that TJ had been involved in an incident. The secretary was soft-spoken, and since I was also back to school and taking the call in my classroom, it was hard to hear what she was saying. I thought she said something about TJ taking another student's lunch because he said we had not given him money. This was totally untrue, but I just played it off and told her I would make sure from now on he had lunch money.

"A month later, we received another call. The school secretary, Ms. Ransom, said she was calling to inform us of another incident involving TJ. It was just before Halloween, and apparently, TJ had gotten the candy we had bought to pass out to trick-or-treaters, taken it to school, and was caught selling it to the students during lunch. She said they were sending home a letter by TJ stating that he was being suspended for one day and that we would need to make arrangements to have him stay home the next day. When I later confronted TJ about the incident, his customary 'I don't know' was the only response I could elicit.

"Two weeks after the candy-selling incident, I received yet another call, this time from Mr. Rodriguez, vice principal at Belle Aire. His call was regarding TJ disrupting the class during instruction time.

"Apparently, he had stolen the wig his sister had used as part of her Halloween costume, hidden it in his book bag, and taken it into the classroom. Midway through the morning session, he decided to put it on, hop up on his desk, and begin singing and shaking the long hair, pretending he was a popular singer performing and playing a guitar. The class was in an uproar. When the teacher, Miss Suttles, started walking toward him, telling him to get off the desk and sit down, he took off running around the classroom. She was only able to restore order after the front office sent the security officer to haul him out of the classroom. Again, he was suspended.

"I couldn't believe we were only two and a half months into the school year, and TJ had already racked up fifty demerits. Little did I know then that it would only get worse. The lunch money, candy-selling, and wig incidents would be the lesser of the incidents we would have to deal with in the future.

"To say that the 1983–1984 school year was a turbulent year would be an understatement."

FIFTEEN

Out-of-Control Antics

I had allowed Nanna to take another break before continuing her monologue. I knew that she was reliving all that she and Grandpa Dave had gone through. Never in a million years would I have imagined all that had happened with Dad while he was growing up. Yet I was still glad I had chosen to do the research project and learn about my dad's history. With my recording device ready to go, I nodded for Nanna to begin the next phase of sharing.

"I am going to skip ahead to February of the 1985–86 school year when your dad was in seventh grade. I was in the middle of teaching my third period class one morning when I got a call from the secretary at Belle Aire. She stated that Mr. Rodriguez, the vice principal, needed for me to come to the school that afternoon, and it was imperative that I be there by 4:00. When I inquired as to the reason for this sudden meeting, she said that I would be meeting with someone named Mr. Bryant who had to be back in Los Angeles for a 6:00 meeting.

I asked who Mr. Bryant was, but she was unable to provide any additional information.

"Traffic was terrible as I left the high school where I taught and tried to maneuver the car through the afternoon rush-hour. I was determined to stay calm. Who on earth was this Mr. Bryant, and why was there such a rush for me to meet with him? Anyway, with three minutes to spare, I rounded the circular driveway leading to the school, parked, jumped out, lifted my head to try and look as confident as I possibly could, and walked into the school at exactly 3:59. Vice Principal Rodriguez met me with an outstretched hand as I entered his office and introduced me to Mr. Bryant who I assumed was someone affiliated with the school. Looking back on it, though, his corporate America business attire should have told me differently.

"As we were about to be seated, the after-school detention supervisor escorted TJ into the office. How could one child be required to serve so many detentions? There had to be a seat in the detention hall with TJ's name on it because he practically lived there. Anyway, back to the situation at hand. As soon as the supervisor exited the office, Mr. Rodriguez wasted no time in informing us of the purpose of the meeting.

"Mr. Bryant lived in the area and had a child who attended Belle Aire. Several days prior, Mr. Bryant and some friends had been playing a game of pick-up basketball on Belle Aire's basketball court around 5:00 in the afternoon. Before starting the game, they had put their wallets in their jacket pockets or underneath their jackets and laid them at the edge of the court. TJ and a couple of his buddies had been messing around the school campus while the men were playing. When they finished their game and started to leave, Mr. Bryant noticed his wallet was missing.

"The men had seen several boys in the vicinity while they were playing and figured one of them had stolen his wallet. He said he had several twenties and some ones in the wallet, but that was not his biggest concern. He was more concerned about his driver's license and several credit cards, including his company's Gold American Express card. The following morning he notified the school and offered a $100 reward for the return of the wallet with the license and credit cards. Reward flyers were also placed on several telephone poles and in windows of stores in the area.

"Meanwhile, the same afternoon that the wallet went missing, TJ and his buddies had paid a visit to the mini-market inside the Chevron gas station two blocks away from Belle Aire. The clerk remembered the boys buying over $20 worth of candy, and that one of the boys kept pulling twenties out of a brown wallet that also contained what looked like several credit cards in the card slots.

"When he jokingly asked the boy holding the wallet if he had stolen his dad's wallet, he answered, 'Oh no, I wouldn't do anything like that because my dad would kill me. My birthday was yesterday, and my parents gave me a wallet with some money in it as a birthday gift. They even put some pretend credit cards in it to make me feel grownup.' The clerk thought it a bit strange, but his answer sounded plausible, so he let it go. Besides, what young kid like this boy would make up a story like that?

"He thought no more about it until someone posted the reward flyer in the gas station window the following day. He immediately called the number on the flyer to report what he had witnessed and told them he could definitely identify the boy with the wallet and, if necessary, the other two boys with him.

"Now here we were, addressing the incident of the wallet theft. My mind had drifted off for a minute but snapped back to attention when Mr. Rodriguez mentioned something about TJ collecting the reward. 'What?' I asked, embarrassed that I had not been paying attention. 'Would you please repeat that again because I want to make sure I heard correctly what you just shared.'

'Sure,' he said. 'This morning after we put up the reward posters and made an announcement on the PA system, TJ came into the office with the wallet. He said he had found it down by the creek that runs behind the school, and even though it was a little wet from being near the creek, it was still good, and all the cards and license were in it. He didn't know what happened to the money. He said he was turning it in so he could get the $100 reward.' Mrs. Ransom, our school secretary who was unaware of the call from the gas station clerk, excitedly took the wallet, wrote down TJ's name and classroom teacher's name, and said she would alert Mr. Bryant and have the reward waiting for him after school.

"I sat there in utter shock. My mind was racing as I thought, *So, if I'm understanding this correctly, my son stole the man's wallet, then turned around and was trying to collect the reward for stealing the wallet? Huh?* It would have been hysterically funny if it hadn't been the millionth time he had pulled such an unbelievable antic.

"We all turned to TJ, and as I opened my mouth to ask,

'TJ, why did you do that?' I already knew the answer. That boy said, 'I don't know' so much that I'm certain he was the only child in seventh grade whose communications skills were limited to a seven-word vocabulary: 'I don't know, and I didn't do it.' Little did I know that a similar scene would be repeated in this very office two weeks later.

"That evening, rather than face the music and his dad's wrath, TJ decided he would run away. I figured he had taken off for the mall and went looking for him there. However, after checking the arcade and walking the length of the mall several times, I decided to go back home just in case he had returned, About half an hour later, I received a call from the Puente Hills Mall Security Office telling me they had my son in custody.

"The minute I walked into the office, I took one look at TJ and burst out laughing uncontrollably. In fact, I laughed so hard that tears started rolling down my face. Once I was able to settle down, breathe, and gain some composure, one of the security officers asked me if I knew why TJ had shown up at the mall barefooted. I said plain and simply, 'He did not want to face his dad.'

"I explained that he had been involved in another incident at his school earlier in the day. To my knowledge, TJ had been in the backyard playing with the dog when he heard his dad drive up. In his haste to get away before Dave got in the house, he took off running and went out the side gate without his shoes.

"The officer took over from there. 'Well, according to TJ, once he got here, he was told he could not be in the mall or go into the Arcade without shoes because that was the mall's policy. So being the boy who always comes up with a plan, he decided he would sneak back into the mall by coming in with a large group of shoppers.

"'Once in, he headed for one of the stores that display shoes on a rack just outside of their front door. He said he was going to grab a pair of shoes from the display rack and take off so that he could go into the arcade. However, one of the clerks had noticed him hanging around looking at the shoes, and as he went to grab a pair, the clerk started yelling and running toward him. In his haste to get away, TJ grabbed two mix-matched shoes and took off. He was probably also unaware that stores don't display matching pairs for the reason that someone could come up and steal them.'

"Mall security had been alerted about the theft, and the clerk was able to tell the officers exactly which shoes were missing from the display. He was also able to give them TJ's description, so they knew exactly who they were looking for. Within ten minutes, they had easily apprehended him. They figured he would probably head to the arcade, so they took a walk through that area and noticed this kid matching TJ's description going from game to game with a slight limp.

"When they looked down at his feet, they saw he was wearing two left shoes. The brown leather shoe on his right foot looked to be two sizes too big, which caused him to limp as he shuffled his right foot along the floor. On his left foot was the white, orange, and blue canvas shoe that was a size too small, so he was walking on the back of it with his heel hanging over.

"Totally exasperated over TJ's behavior, Dave and I immediately contacted Dr. Sheldon's office to try to set up another appointment. However, we were told that Dr. Sheldon had retired and no longer worked there. We asked if he had appointed a replacement and was told that his patients were now being seen by a Dr. Donald Moore.

"The receptionist proudly informed me that Dr. Moore was one of the top child psychologists in the state and that she would be more than happy to make an appointment for us. When I asked his hourly rate, the figure she quoted knocked me of my chair. Once I recovered, I responded, 'Oh, I just want my son to see ONE doctor, not the entire team.'

"The first few visits seemed to go well. When he would leave the office, TJ would be upbeat and talkative after his sessions with Dr. Moore. I started to believe that he would live up to his reputation and actually be worth the exorbitant fee he was charging. However, several months into TJ's therapy sessions, I began having some doubts, and one afternoon purely by accident, my doubts were confirmed.

"On this particular day, I was up in our bedroom cleaning. Since the bedroom windows overlook the pool, I can clearly hear everything that is said in that area. TJ didn't see me or realize that I could hear him.

"He was talking to one of his friends who had come over to shoot hoops in our backyard when I overheard TJ saying, 'Yeah, man, this dude that I have to go see every week keeps asking me the same ole dumb questions about how I'm doing with my behavior in school, and I just tell him what I think he wants to hear.

"'You should see him smile and nod his head like one of them bobble-head dolls when I'm just making up some stuff and telling him. I even told him that the teacher has a behavior chart with different colors and that I'm now getting purple stickers for outstanding behavior and blue for excellent. Just to make it a little more believable, I told him that I did get one yellow sticker last week, which was a "Try Harder" sticker. When I left his office, I just fell out laughing. Man, that dude was funny and kinda dumb because you can tell him anything, and he just grins, nods, and believes it.'

"'What!' I screamed so loudly that I'm surprised the boys didn't hear me. 'You mean, we are racking up thousands of dollars in therapy bills when all he is doing is feeding Dr. Moore a bunch of lies?' When I later shared with Dave what I had overheard TJ tell his friend, we decided to book an extra family session with Dr. Moore and see what his response would be. Before we could meet with him, though, I received a very disturbing call from Belle Aire, again.

"It was 10:43 on a Thursday morning during fourth period when the phone in my classroom rang. My student assistant, Steve, answered the phone, then announced that someone from Belle Aire School was calling.

"Before I could get to the back of the room to take the call, some of my students began saying, 'What's TJ done now?' I was told that there was a problem at the school with TJ and that I needed to get there ASAP. Luckily, my lunch period was immediately after fourth period, and my preparation period followed lunch, so that gave me an hour and twenty-five minutes, enough time to run to Belle Aire and return to the high school in time to teach my sixth and seventh period classes.

"Upon arriving at Belle Aire, this was the scenario I was given. The students had been released around 10:00 for morning nutritional break. Apparently, an argument between TJ and another student had been brewing during the break, and it continued once they returned to the classroom. Mrs. Baker, their teacher, had heard some of the students discussing the argument while standing at the door as the students entered. Once all students were seated and instructed to return to working on their math worksheets, TJ decided he was going to start making comments about the boy under his breath.

"When asked to stop, he began to sass Mrs. Baker. After a few minutes of exhibiting this disruptive and disrespectful behavior, Mrs. Baker called the office to notify the assistant principal in charge of discipline that she was sending TJ to the office. She completed a form noting why she was recommending him for discipline, handed the form to TJ, and sent him to the office.

"However, once TJ left the classroom, he headed in the opposite direction of the office and towards the back of the school. His intent was to sneak off into the wooded area behind the school and hang out until school was out when he could go home. As he passed the open area at the end of the wing where his classroom was located, he noticed a ladder leaning against the roof.

"Figuring he now had a way of getting back at Mrs. Baker for sending him to the office, he quickly climbed up the ladder, ran across the flat roof to the approximate area where he thought his classroom was located, and began tap dancing and singing as loudly as he possibly could. This not only disrupted Mrs. Baker's classroom but the adjacent classrooms as well.

"After a few minutes of this, the office secretary was able

to locate the custodian and instructed him to get TJ off the roof immediately. Problem was that TJ was a lot younger, faster, and quicker than the custodian, so for the next ten minutes or so, TJ raced back and forth across the roof as the custodian chased and tried to catch him.

"He even resorted to jumping the short distance across the area that separated a couple of the other wings. Realizing that the custodian was not going to be able to catch him, the school finally resorted to calling the fire department to come and get him off the roof. When TJ heard the fire truck siren, he ran around the custodian, scampered down the ladder, managed to get off the school grounds, and disappeared into the woods by the time the firemen arrived.

"After leaving Belle Aire, I was so mentally and emotionally exhausted that I called my high school and told them I would not be able to return and to get someone to cover my sixth and seventh period classes. I went home, asked the sitter who watched Mother during the day to stay and leave at her regular time, went upstairs to my bedroom, got into bed, and crawled up into the fetal position. Apparently, I drifted off into a fitful sleep because the next thing I remember was hearing the front door open and close, indicating that Lynn was home from school. Now, if only TJ would show up.

"Several minutes later, I heard the doorbell ring and heard his voice as his sister opened the door to let him in. Both were surprised when I walked into the family room since I usually didn't get home until an hour later. I explained that I had needed to take care of some business that afternoon and had only worked half a day.

"TJ wasn't quite sure if the school had notified me about

his latest caper, so he was being a bit cautious. Still, he tried to act like everything was normal as he sat at the counter eating a peanut butter and jelly sandwich. When I asked to see what he had to do for homework that evening, he quickly manufactured his next tall tale.

"'Mom, this morning when I was walking to school, one of the big football players that goes to Johnston High School walked up and threatened to beat me up if I didn't give him my backpack. So, I did. It had all my books, my homework from last night, and my lunch in it. I didn't bring my homework home today because I didn't have a book to work out of.'

"Lacking the energy to deal with him at this point, and with Dave out of town, I simply turned and walked away to calm myself and to keep from knocking him into the middle of next week, as people in the South would say. On my way back up the stairs, I couldn't help but see his sister standing in the hallway rolling her eyes and shaking her head as if to say, 'Here we go again!'

"'Lordy be!' I could hear my mother say if I had ever done anything like that. 'Child, what am I gonna do with you?'

"Two months later, almost to the day of the tap-dancing incident, Dave and I were sitting in the same office but this time speaking to Principal Matthews, Vice Principal Rodriguez, Psychologist Waterman, and teachers Warren, Williams, and Thomas. Once the meeting got underway, it was obvious that TJ was being expelled from Belle Aire, and this little group was making certain they had dotted all their I's and crossed all their T's.

"The list containing the evidence of why TJ could no longer attend that school included:

9/25 Bus citation—TJ hit student in the head with an umbrella. Transportation privilege suspended until citation signed. Citation never returned, but TJ involved in sports so seldom rides the bus.

10/20 Student suspended.

10/27 Referral—TJ threw a backpack belonging to another student into a ditch filled with water and ruining $55 worth of books. TJ's parents need to replace textbooks as soon as possible.

10/30 Referral—suggested leniency by Mrs. Johansenn due to incomplete work. TJ failed to come for detention to complete work.

11/14 Bus citation—Bus driver returned load of students to school due to unruly behavior. TJ had been involved in fighting and cursed at the bus driver. Transportation privileges are suspended for remainder of semester. Called mother.

. . .

11/28 End of second grading period. TJ has a C in citizenship and a C average in academics.

1/13 Referral—Mr. Williams, teacher, said TJ still hasn't returned unsatisfactory progress report given the week before. TJ said he lost it and needed a new one. Ten demerits have been taken from citizenship grade.

1/15 Referral—Mrs. Warren says a fight between TJ and another student occurred after a couple of days of verbal taunting and jostling between them. TJ yelled profanity across the room to another student. Mr. Matthews, the principal, helped them to work out the problem. Threatened them with suspension if problem continued. Ten demerits were taken from citizenship grade.

1/23 TJ forced another student to give him $9.75. He said he would beat him up if he didn't. Principal Matthews contacted parents and suspended TJ for one day.

1/30 End of third grading period. F in citizenship due to two office referrals and seven incidents of tardies and/or failure to bring materials to class. D average grade, which makes him ineligible for sports, etc.

. . .

2/11 Referral—Mr. Thomas, teacher, said TJ did not complete a two-week assignment and did not stay for detention to complete it. TJ also took another student's work, erased the student's name, put his name on it, and turned it in as his work. Ten demerits from his citizenship grade.

2/17 Mr. Thomas, teacher, says TJ still has not completed the work. TJ told him he's working on it.

2/22 Referral—Mrs. Odem, teacher, said that TJ took $2.00 from another student. She told him to give the money back, which he did. Then, he took it again after she left. TJ later said he was just playing around, and when he tried to give it back, the student would not accept it. TJ said he meant to give it back the next day, but three days later, the boy still has not received the money. On 3/5, Mrs. Odem reminded TJ about the money, and he said, 'Oh, yeah, I know I still owe him the money.'

2/24 Referral—Mrs. Montique, teacher, said TJ left chorus class to get a drink without permission. TJ said he was told to pick up some stuff from the floor and throw it away. Since there was no trash can nearby, he went outside to throw it away and get a drink. When he returned, he was asked where he had been, and he responded, 'To get a drink.' Teacher suggested a parent conference because TJ cannot be allowed to just do as he pleases, especially with a student teacher starting to work with the group. Mrs. Montique sent a note home asking the mother to contact her. Principal Matthews suggested Mrs. Montique contact the mother directly.

2/27 Referral—Mr. Harisomi, teacher, said TJ received five demerits for hitting another student and another five demerits for falsifying his homeroom teacher's signature.

3/5 Mrs. Tenaki, teacher, brought in a cassette player that she had taken away from TJ since students are not allowed to have them at school.

3/5 Office secretary gave TJ a letter to give to his parents informing them that he was at the D-level in citizenship for the fourth grading period.

3/5 Mrs. Tenaki, teacher, said TJ had not come for detention. He had been given two days to make it up at lunch or after school. He called his father and told him he had to stay that day to make it up, which he did.

3/6 When asked for the D-level citizenship letter, TJ said he hadn't gotten it signed yet. He said he'd fallen asleep around 5:00 doing his homework.

· · ·

3/6 Referral—Mr. Harisomi, teacher, said TJ was disobeying and being defiant by not doing as directed and continued to do as he pleased. Called mother and suspended TJ for defiance. Ten demerits from citizenship grade. Mr. Rodriguez, vice principal, informed mother that TJ was down to the F-level in citizenship.

3/6 (After school) Mr. Redmond brought in TJ's math book, which was totally demolished. He had also found TJ's 'D' citizenship letter that had been sent to his parents stuck in between the pages of the book. It was clear that TJ had forged his father's signature on the letter.

3/10 Referral—At 12:00 noon ,TJ left campus without permission and went to Thrifty's to buy $2.50 worth of ice cream and seltzer. Ten demerits taken from his Citizenship grade and referral sent home for parents' signature.

3/11 Referral—At 1:00 p.m., Mrs. Gardner, teacher, called office to say she had sent TJ to the office about five minutes ago. He still had not arrived. TJ had been sent to the office to do his work since he had come to class unprepared. Seventh period teacher reported TJ had not shown up for his class either. About 1:30, TJ showed up for that class and was sent to principal's office. TJ told Principal Matthews that he had been out looking for his book that someone stole. Principal requested meeting with parents on 3/12.

. . .

3/11 Letter prepared for parent conference containing the following information: End of fourth grading period; F grade in citizenship due to three office referrals; five tardies or materials not brought to class; three eating or gum chewing in class; and two demerits for hitting or kicking. He had also turned in two merits that had been forged.

"Once Dave and I had finished reading the list of incidents, Mr. Matthews began providing a summary of TJ's record since his arrival at Belle Aire.

"'TJ began attending Belle Aire when he was in fourth grade. He left and returned again during the 1985–1986 school year, and during both attendance periods, he exhibited some severe behavioral problems. He returned in the middle of sixth grade and seemed to have a good attitude and have a good semester here at the school. This year, however, as a seventh grader, he has attended regularly, but incidents of misbehavior have escalated, and his school performance has declined.

"'As of yesterday, 3/11, we've made the decision that TJ can no longer attend Belle Aire. We have contacted a neighboring alternative school who will allow him to attend—with conditions. We have provided you with the school's information and recommend that you contact them immediately so there will be very little interruption in TJ's education process.'

"Walking to the car following the meeting, Dave and I made the decision to head immediately to Royal Heights

School, the alternative school recommended by Principal Matthews at Belle Aire.

"We pulled into the parking lot, found a place to park, and were walking toward what we thought was the entrance when a lady said if we were looking for the entrance, we needed to turn around and go in the opposite direction. Before we could turn around, she asked if we were there to enroll our son. We answered yes, and she advised us to first go home, look on the internet, and learn more about the school. She suggested even talking to some other parents before enrolling TJ.

"Following her advice and checking parent's postings about the school, we realized that the environment at Royal Heights would probably exacerbate the misbehavior problems rather than provide solutions for them.

"I looked at Dave and asked, 'Where do we go now?' *Oh Lord*, I thought, *why do we keep ending up going around the same round-about trying to figure which road to exit next?*"

SIXTEEN

From Silly to Serious

"T he question of which road to take next was decided for us when TJ ran away from home again on Friday, March 21st. I remember it well because Dave and I were supposed to be attending a formal dinner dance. I was running late because of a hair appointment that ran almost an hour behind, and by the time I fought Friday evening traffic to get home, I only had thirty minutes to get dressed and in the car.

"Since Lynn was now almost seventeen, we didn't have to worry about getting sitters anymore. We made sure she had the phone number to the hotel in Huntington Beach where the event was being held in case of an emergency. Our last instructions to TJ were 'behave for your sister, go in every once in a while to see about Grandma and get her some water if she wants some, and you can watch TV or play your games. There are snacks in the frig and in the pantry, but don't be a hog and eat up everything. Are those instructions clear?'

"He managed to mumble a 'Yes Mom,' as we headed out the door."

"Dave and I were just finishing eating our main course and waiting for dessert to be served when one of the waiters came to our table and asked if there was a Dave or Beetrice Ferguson here. We looked at each other before raising our hands. The waiter leaned over and said there was a call for either one of us at the front desk. Dave immediately got up and went to take the call while I mentally began preparing for another shoe to drop. When he returned a couple of minutes later, he merely said, 'We have an emergency at home and need to leave now.'

"Apparently, soon after we had left the house, TJ told Lynn he was tired and was going upstairs to his room to take a nap. He then slipped around the corner and out the patio door in the dining room and took off. About ninety minutes later, the police called the house and said they had TJ in custody. That's when she had called the hotel to notify us.

"The hour drive back to Hacienda Heights and to the police station was a tense and nervous one, for we had no idea what trouble TJ had gotten into. Neither of us mentioned the fact that we had just been robbed of the one chance we had had in ages to get away and have a night of fun and relaxation. However, it was certainly in the back of our minds.

"Unfortunately, we had been to that police station so many times that most of the staff knew us by name. When we arrived, we were told to go to a room in the back of the station. We sat down, and one of the officers proceeded to tell us what had happened.

"This time, TJ had headed to Moorlands RV Dealers on

Colima Road, gone into one of the RVs that was unlocked, and done some damage to the interior. There was no way he was going to be released this time to come home with us. Since it was the weekend, we would have to wait until Monday when he would appear in front of the judge. Until then, he would have to spend the weekend at the detention center in La Puente.

"This was the first time TJ had not been released to us and allowed to come home. My heart was breaking, even though I knew it would only be a matter of time before he would cross that line, and this would happen. As I looked at TJ and his eyes met mine, he immediately looked away and shifted his focus elsewhere. I began asking myself, 'What on earth is going on in his head that causes him to continue doing things like this, even going out of his way sometimes to deceive, defy, and destroy?'

"The next morning, Dave and I went to visit the RV dealer and spoke to the manager about the vandalism committed by our son. When shown the damaged RV, I had a flashback of TJ destroying his stuffed animals: a leg here, an arm there, and stuffing everywhere. It was like he had used some kind of sharp instrument to cut, scratch, and destroy seat cushions, cabinets, and bedding. The RV was a mess.

"The manager's comment, 'Boy, your son must really have been angry at someone or something to do this kind of damage,' confirmed what I had long suspected. Even though he was so young he could not articulate his feelings when he had been abused in the foster homes, he subconsciously remembered it. I don't think he even realized that he was still suffering from that abuse, and thus was constantly lashing out and responding to his anger and frustration.

"We asked the manager to get a quote on the cost of the damages and agreed to pay for repairs and replacements. In return, he agreed not to file charges.

"On Monday during the detention hearing, Judge Martin noted that Moorland RV Dealer had notified the court that they were not filing charges, so TJ would no longer be detained. However, because of his history of run-ins with law enforcement officers, he would not be allowed to return home. Instead, he was being placed in a group home in Apple Valley and would remain there for the next six months. Judge Martin also informed us that he was appointing a Guardian ad Litem to work with TJ and our family and try to help resolve some of the issues.

"Following the hearing, I asked one of the officers what was a Guardian ad Litem, since I was not familiar with the term. She informed me that a GAL, as they are called, was a person appointed by the court to investigate and find options for dealing with a troubled youth's problems. The main focus was always 'what's in the best interest of the child, or youth in this case.' Therefore, the GAL would be visiting and working directly with TJ at the group home, visiting our home and interviewing us, determining the dynamics of the relationship between TJ and Lynn, speaking with schoolteachers and staff, talking with our pastor, determining where TJ should live most of the time, and assessing our mental and financial stability.

"*Wow,* I thought as I walked away, *he or she must be some kind of super-person. Good luck in getting TJ to cooperate and tell you the truth rather than stuff he makes up as he goes along.*

"Michael, I hate to tell you this, but your dad's stay at Apple Valley group home was short-lived. He did manage to last three weeks, though, before the group home supervisor said she had had enough and that TJ had to go. During his first week there, he managed to coerce a couple of the kids at the home to be his flunkies. They would steal things for him, take the rap for devious acts he committed, and refuse to tattle on him.

"Because TJ was getting away with this, he started pushing the envelope more and by the second week was slipping out of bed during the night and running around the street, vandalizing people's property. The third week when he attempted to burn down the home, they had had enough. So, they sent him back home to us.

"He had only been back home three weeks when he did something that surpassed anything he had done up to that point. The story made the 'Breaking News' category on the 11:00 news on both Channel 2 and Channel 4. It also made the front page of our local newspaper. 'Boy stuck in chimney until rescued by fireman.' However, I like the heading used in our little neighborhood newspaper better. It read, 'Boy stuck in chimney realizes he's not Santa.'

"It all came about this way. Dave had reprimanded TJ for throwing the family dog in the pool, so he decided to run away—again. We called and alerted the local law enforcement office that he was gone and to be on the lookout for him. Little did we know that before he ran away, he had stashed a blanket and some food under a couple of peach trees in our backyard, right outside the windows to Mother's room.

"We figured he had headed back to the mall again, which was his usual modus operandi, and sure enough, he had done just that. When the mall closed at 9:00, he had sneaked back into the yard. Apparently, after a while, he got cold and scared. At first, he tried knocking on Mother's window to get her to open the front door and let him in. After having no luck there and trying all the doors and finding them locked, he climbed up on the roof and tried to get in by coming down the chimney.

"All of a sudden, his dad and I heard all this screaming and banging and soon realized it was echoing from the family room fireplace. We immediately recognized TJ's voice and asked where he was. 'I'm stuck in the chimney' came his faint reply. His answer was both a relief that he was okay but also another slap in the face, and another crisis situation created by his antics. We let out a collective sigh, shook our heads, then frantically dialed 9-1-1 to report our son stuck in the chimney.

"Suddenly, our home and neighborhood were transformed from a typical quiet and peaceful suburban one to the midway during peak hours at the local carnival. Minutes after the 9-1-1 call, the fire truck arrived with siren blaring, light flashing, and firemen running with a ladder and axes. Close behind were news vans from Channel 2 and Channel 4 flooding the neighborhood with lights, cameras, and news reporters.

"It was like a three-ring circus taking place on our block at 10:00 at night, and we were feeling like the clowns. To add to the circus-like atmosphere, not only were all the neighbors out trying to see what was going on, but since our house was located near a busy intersection, numerous lookey-lous had either stopped their cars in the middle of the street or had parked and walked up to get a better look at what was going on.

"Less than an hour later following his extrication from the chimney, a scared, soot-covered, scratched-up TJ sat on a stool at our kitchen counter. When asked why he did it, he proceeded to give me, his dad, and the firemen his usual puppy-dog eyes look and his familiar 'I don't know' answer. The night ended with the firemen handing us a notice stating our house had been condemned because they had had to destroy the chimney in order to get him out.

"Bricks and pieces of the chimney were left precariously hanging, and we were told that it must be repaired immediately. Much to our chagrin, the incident, along with our faces, were plastered across the screen on the 11:00 news that evening and the national news the following day. Across the country, friends and relatives familiar with TJ's antics soon began calling to confirm that it was indeed him who had been stuck.

"After putting TJ in the shower, having him scrub the soot off himself, and putting ointment on the scratches, I sent him to bed. We thought that was the end of the matter. Little did we know that early the next evening, we would answer the door and find two policemen and a Child Protective Services representative stand there inquiring if we were the parents of TJ.

"When we answered, 'Yes,' they said they were there to arrest us for child abuse and to take TJ and his sister into protective services. Needless to say, we were floored, and all we could do was ask, 'What! Are! You! Talking! About?'

"For the next few minutes, the CPS representative explained that when TJ had gone to school the next day, his teacher inquired as to how he had gotten all the scratches and bruises. His response was that we had beaten him and thrown him out of the house and that he had to sleep outdoors in the backyard all night.

"He even told his teacher that if she didn't believe him, she could come to our house and look out in our backyard and see the blanket and food we had given him when we had thrown him out. Since it was the teacher's job to report any suspected cases of abuse, CPS was called, and a report was made to the police. The police had immediately come to the house while we were at work and the kids at school, checked, and found the blanket and food in the backyard under the bush just as TJ had reported, then returned later on in the evening to arrest us.

"When Dave and I finally collected our thoughts, we invited them to come in. We turned on the news clip recording we had made from one of Channel 2's previous airings, then sat back and watched them as the reporter commented on the boy who had been stuck in the chimney and how he was fortunate to have only sustained some cuts, scratches and bruises.

"With a picture of our house in the background, the camera panned to the destroyed chimney while the reporter followed with the comment, 'As you can see, the chimney didn't fare as well as the boy.' It was almost comical to watch their faces turn red and jaws drop to the floor as light started to dawn. Needless to say, they soon made a hasty, embarrassed, and apologetic exit.

"For the next several days, Dave and I laid low, for how could we show our faces to our neighbors after the chimney incident? When we had to go out, we would open the garage door, back the cars straight out of the garage, and head down the street.

"When we returned, we would hit the garage door opener, drive right back into the garage, and quickly close the door. We were avoiding the neighbors at all cost. To have the fire truck, Channel 2 and Channel 4 news vans, and then a police cruiser and a CPS marked car parked in front of our house within a twenty-hour period was a bit too much for our quiet and peaceful little neighborhood. Neighbors couldn't help but wonder, *Who was this family that had moved here from Illinois and whose son was wreaking total havoc?*

"Following the visit by the police and CPS representative, reality hit, and I finally broke down. Months of dealing with TJ's antics, the challenges presented by Mother's dementia, compounded by problems arising with our marriage had all become overwhelming. Feeling totally devastated, I knocked on Mother's door, went into her room, sat down on the floor in front of her as she sat in her rocking chair, laid my head in her lap, and just cried my heart out.

"Even though she was now ninety-seven, she was still Muh Dear to me when I was hurting. I desperately needed the same comfort and reassurance she had given me as a child. She was now constantly dealing with her dementia, but there were times when her mind was as clear as a bell. During those times, she was the same source of wisdom and comfort she had been when I was growing up. I now prayed that, if only for a brief period of time, she would be in a lucid state of mind. Thank God she was!

"Being the wise woman she had always been, she simply allowed me to cry to my heart's content. She didn't interrupt or try to talk to me but rather gently stroked my head with those same veined, gnarled, and blessed hands that had ministered the poultice and saved my life forty-one years earlier. As she rocked back and forth ever so slightly, the motion was soothing.

"When the emotional storm had subsided, I was finally able to collect my thoughts and speak. I attempted to share the details of our most recent and humiliating visit from the police and CPS worker. Mother looked me straight in the eye as only she could do and began speaking. You know, the advice she gave still has a profound effect on me today, and that took place thirty-three years ago. I can still hear her speaking.

"'Baby, you remember when you were little, and you used to sit on that stool in the corner of the kitchen, and we would talk while I ironed the white folks' clothes? Well, I'm gonna tell you the same thing again that I told you then, and maybe now it'll make more sense. You were near death when we got you, and Lord knows there were times when your daddy and I thought you weren't gonna make it. But you did—praise the Lord! And I used to tell you that the Lord had a reason for sparing your life.

"'I feel it was because He had something special for you to do while you're still on this earth, and I knew it was supposed to be about helping other people. I see it clearly now. This poor child you adopted has got tons of problems, or else he wouldn't be acting all crazy like he is. But you can't give up on him! You've got to hang in there with him.

"'Sit him down when you're not so frustrated with him and let him talk to you. Ask him what he is trying to get away from when he runs away. Ask him if he is trying to get away from something that is bothering him. Ask him if he's scared of something and is too afraid to tell you about it. Ask him what you and his dad can do to help him not to want to do those things. Most of all, though, just keep praying for him and loving him unconditionally. I can't dwell on that enough. Keep on loving him the way the good Lord loves us.

"'Going back to when you were a little girl, I remember when your daddy and I were trying to get you well and help you deal with all the hurt and pain and struggles you were going through after the poisoning. It seemed like it was just one thing after another after another. When we thought we had one thing licked, here comes something else. But one look at you and your big ole eyes, and we knew we just had to keep on doing everything we could to get you well and healthy.

"'I can remember your daddy asking other baggage porters down at the train station to let him work in their place if they had to take off so he could get extra money for your doctor bills. 'Round about that time, he also started cutting the white folks' grass and doing odd jobs on the weekends so he could make more extra money. That man sure did love him some Little Bee right on up until the day he died.

"'So now, it's your turn. TJ's got some real bad problems, and most of it's not his fault. I can't even imagine what that child went through and how much he suffered in those foster homes when he was too little to fight back. God only knows what he is still suffering, and who knows if he will ever completely get over it.

"'But you still can't give up on him. And I'll say it one more time. Put your arms around him, hug him, and smother him with as much love as you've got, no matter what kind of crazy stuff he does. Most of all, though, stay on your knees and pray because God can work Himself some miracles. He saved your life, and that wasn't nothing but a miracle. A mighty miracle at that! Oh yes, He can work Himself some mighty good miracles!'

"That was Muh Dear's final piece of advice to me. Several days later, she suffered a second stroke, and I could no longer take care of her at home. The last thing I wanted to do was to put her in a nursing home again, yet I had to face reality and realize I had no other option. Working a full-time job teaching; directing several school choirs and a church choir; taking care of your grandfather, your dad, and your aunt Lynn; and managing a household went far beyond multi-tasking.

"So, again with a heavy heart, I started looking to find a facility that would treat her like the diamond she still was in my heart."

SEVENTEEN

The Interview

I had taken Nanna's advice and was now heading to the golf course to play a round of golf with Dad before settling down in the clubhouse to conduct the interview. I felt the interview would work better away from home where my mother and sisters would be present. I wanted Dad to be at a place where he could talk freely and feel relaxed. The game had gone well, especially since Dad had managed to end with a score of eighty-six, beating my ninety. Now, it was time to get down to the business at hand.

"Dad, as I explained earlier, I want to ask you some questions regarding your life from early childhood through your teen years. I'm doing my end-of-the-year project for one of my classes and focusing on my background and family history. I am particularly interested in what you remember about the time you spent in the foster homes.

"I know that in the past, you refused to answer any of my questions, especially after the time we went camping in *northern California, and you had those terrible nightmares. I also know that you've constantly struggled with horrible nightmares while we were growing up. Now that I am older and perhaps mature enough to understand things better, hopefully you will be more willing to share.*

"Meanwhile, Nanna has given me a ton of information, and a lot of it has shocked my socks off. But she felt any information I could get from you would be even more valuable since it would be from your perspective. I'm going to start by asking you to tell me your earliest childhood recollection, either while you were in the foster homes or after you had been adopted."

"I know you're going to laugh, but my earliest memories are of Mom's good ole fried chicken," Dad began. "I remember her standing in the kitchen, putting the chicken in some flour in a brown bag, and shaking it around before putting it in the skillet and frying it. I loved eating the drumstick and would eat so many that my stomach would usually be tight by the time I finished.

"You know, son, looking back on it, I was always insecure about food and felt I needed to protect it until it was eaten. I think I was afraid someone was going to come and snatch it away before I could eat it, and I'd end up hungry. As for the time I was in the foster homes, I don't remember anything."

I didn't really believe that my dad had no memories of his time in the foster homes and thought about pressing the issue. However, I figured I would save those questions until later in the interview when Dad was a little more comfortable talking about his experiences. I jotted down a couple of notes as Dad continued speaking.

"I also remember getting hurt a lot when we lived in Downers Grove and ending up at the Good Samaritan Hospital there. One night, I was down in our family room playing around. Mom was standing over by the fireplace, and I was going to run over and jump on her to give her a goodnight hug. As I started to run, I tripped over a pillow that I had put on the floor earlier and slammed right into the corner of the fireplace. I cut my forehead so badly that blood was everywhere.

"By the time Mom got me to Good Sam's, my blood had completely soaked the bath towel she had told me to hold against the cut. They had to put a bunch of stitches in my head, and as you can see, I still have the scar.

"A year before we moved to California, I remember Dad had his family reunion at our house and his mom, dad, sisters, and brothers came from New York and Michigan. That was so much fun. A lot of my cousins came, and we played on the swing set in our backyard, went to a museum, and Mom had chartered a bus to take us all around Chicago to see different sights. We ended the reunion with a big banquet at one of the well-known restaurants in Downers Grove.

"My fondest memory, though, is when Grandma Sophie, Mom's mother, came to live with us. I used to love sitting and talking to her and listening to her tell Lynn and me about her childhood. I remember one story that she would tell us over and over again about the time when she was seven years old and stole Old Miss Watson's watermelon off her porch.

"Since Grandma was too little to carry the watermelon, she rolled it all the way home and put it out back with a pile of other watermelons her dad had grown and picked. That evening as her mother passed the pile of watermelons, she noticed that one was all dirty and started inquiring as to who put that dirty watermelon in the pile and where did it come from.

"At first, Grandma didn't own up to it, but when her mother threatened to spank all of the children if the guilty person didn't confess, she owned up to stealing it. Her punishment was that she had to roll that watermelon all the way back to Miss Watson's house, knock on her door, and tell her that she had stolen it. As further punishment, she had to offer to help Miss Watson do some chores. Chuckling, Grandma would say, 'I sure learned my lesson about stealing things early in life, and to this day, I have never stolen another thing.' It's too bad I didn't learn that same lesson as easily as Grandma did."

"So, Dad, what were some other memories you had?" I *continued.*

"Well, do you want the good ones or the bad ones first? Because we'll need a whole day and then some if we're going to do the bad ones first. I know, I'm certainly not proud of that, but it is what it is, so I'll have to admit it and move on. Meanwhile, let's continue with some more of the good memories.

"After Dad and Mom bought the motor home, we took all kinds of trips in it. I think the reason they bought it was so Dad could get away from some of the stress he was experiencing on his job. The other reason was that when we traveled, we could take Grandma with us and not have to leave her stuck at home with a sitter. She loved riding in it and used to say all the time that she didn't even know that they made houses that could roll up and down the street.

"I remember one specific time we were preparing to take a trip up to the World's Fair in Vancouver, British Columbia. Since we were going to be doing a lot of bike riding and we also needed to carry Grandma's wheelchair, we had the four bikes in the carrier on the front and the wheelchair carrier on the back.

"When Grandma came out of the house, she saw the wheelchair sitting in the driveway behind the motor home because Dad had not yet put it in the carrier. Grandma started screaming and yelling because she thought we were going to put her in the wheelchair and pull it behind us as we went down the highway. Mom had a hard time convincing her that she was going to ride up front in the motor home just like everybody else. Lynn and I were laughing so hard we were doubled over.

"Another funny incident involving Grandma was when we went to Morro Bay. She was sitting in the wheelchair, and Mom was pushing her to the end of the wharf to get a better look at the big rock that sits in the middle of the bay. For whatever reason, Lynn and I started running, and Mom was trying to keep up with us. She didn't realize the wharf planks were uneven, and one of the wheels caught on one of the uneven planks and almost dumped Grandma on the ground. Mom said she was shaking a week after that happened.

"When we traveled, we would stop at the best Kampgrounds of America, or KOA campsites as they are famously called. We stayed at their campsites all over the United States. I can remember meeting a lot of other kids, going swimming and running around with our dog, Ebony, catching fish in nearby lakes and streams, and Mom cooking the fish for dinner. At one campsite, we parked high up on a hill overlooking the Pacific Ocean, and that was really nice.

"It was kind of scary, though, when Dad was backing into our spot, and it was right on the edge of a cliff. I also remember us visiting Dad's parents in New York and us staying in the motor home instead of in their house. We came back from New York by going through Canada, and it was beautiful up there. You know, son, I think being able to do all those fun things with my family actually helped me start to heal from the bad experiences I had before they adopted me, even though I didn't realize it at the time."

"Okay, Dad. You want to begin on the not-so-good memories now?" I asked, feeling that the next round of testimony was not going to be so easy to relate and possibly would cause Dad some anxiety.

As expected, my dad sighed and responded with, "Yeah, we may as well get started with it. No reason to delay the agony."

"Let me see. Where should I begin? I know Mom has shared a lot with you, but did she tell you about me driving her car when I was about eleven years old?"

"You drove a car at that age?" I responded.

"Well, sorta kinda, but not really. See, this is what happened. Mom had taken Grandma to her doctor's appointment and had stopped on the way home to get Grandma's prescription filled. I don't remember the city, but I do know the drugstore was located on a hill. Mom had left Grandma and me in the car to wait while she ran into the store. As soon as she was out of sight, I got out of the back seat and got in the front behind the wheel. Since Mom had taken the ignition key with her, I had no way to start the engine.

"While I was trying to figure out what I was going to do next, Grandma turned around and said, 'TJ, you know how to drive? Baby, I didn't know you could drive.'

"I immediately responded, 'Yes, ma'am, and I can drive real good.'

"By that time, I had figured that since we were parked on a hill, if I released the emergency brake and messed around with the steering wheel and the gear shift, I could get the car rolling. Within a minute, I had the car moving but then had no idea how I was going to stop it as it picked up speed. Just at the moment when I started to panic, the car hit the cement median strip, jumped up on the curb, and came to a stop as the back tire came to rest against the curb.

"The car was inches away from going out into the busy intersection where we could have been hit from both directions by cross traffic. Seconds later, Mom came running up to the car, screaming and crying hysterically. I wish I could say that that was the last such incident, but in fact, I was just getting started."

"Oh my goodness, Dad! Both you and Great-Grandma Sophie could have been killed!" I said as I shook my head vehemently. "Dad, that act goes far beyond your not-so-good antics. That one is down-right bad and scary," I continued.

"Yeah, I know," Dad responded.

"Well, to continue, there were things I did that were not as bad and not as scary. For example, I used to love running off and going down to the movie theater near my house. Since I didn't have money most of the time, I would go up to the ticket window and tell the lady or man that I had to use the bathroom.

"Most of the time, they would let me go in. Once inside, I would sneak into one theater, watch that movie, then sneak into another one. Sometimes when I was supposed to be in school, I would spend the entire day at the theater and come home around the time I would be getting home from school. When I got home, I would wait until Lynn was upstairs or in the bathroom to check the message machine on the phone. If the school had called to say I had been absent, I would just erase the message before Mom got home.

"Another thing I remember doing was sneaking my dad's trumpet out of the house and hiding it under a bush in the backyard. After everyone left the house for work or school, I went back to the house, got the trumpet and his sweater, and had planned to take them to school. To this day, I have no idea why I took Dad's sweater.

"My initial plan was just to show the trumpet off to all my friends, but then I got what I thought was a better idea. Why not ditch school altogether, take the trumpet to a pawn shop, and sell it? That way, I would have some money to spend and share with my friends. I was always wanting to buy stuff for my friends. I think subconsciously I was trying to buy their friendship because I had this desperate need to be liked and accepted, to feel like I belonged. In fact, I would sit and think of ways to get things I could give to them.

"Unfortunately, my plan for the trumpet didn't work out. The owner of the pawn shop said first he needed identification with my name and address that proved I was eighteen years old or older, and second, he needed to see papers that showed I was the rightful owner of the trumpet before he could give me some money for it. I just turned around, walked out, and took the trumpet back home where I put it back in Dad's closet. I don't remember what happened to the sweater.

"Speaking of getting money, that reminds me of a time when I actually came up with a scheme where I did get some money. When Mom and Dad went to Europe and came back, they had some foreign currency left over from the trip. They had saved several bills from France, England, Switzerland, Germany, and one other country which I can't remember right now.

"However, they had quite a bit of money left over from Belgium, and a couple of my friends and I used to play with it when they came over. One day, my friend said, 'TJ, too bad this money ain't real, because if it was, we'd have us some money to buy stuff.' That got me thinking. The money was real, but because it was from other countries, it looked like fake money to them. I had an idea.

"The next day, which was Saturday, I told Mom I was going to my friend Robbie's house but instead took off for the bank. Mom and Dad banked at Alameda Bank, and since I would go into the bank with Mom a lot of times when she did her banking, most of the tellers knew me. So when I walked in, I looked for one of the tellers who had helped Mom when I would come in with her. I got into that line, and when it was my turn, I moved up to her window."

The lady smiled and said, 'Hello, TJ, where is your mom today?'

I immediately responded, "Oh, she's sitting out in the car,

but she hurt her foot, and it's hard for her to walk, so she sent me in to take care of the banking for her.

"'Oh, I see,' the teller responded. 'I certainly hope she feels better. So, how can I help you?'

"Well, when my mom and dad went to Europe, they had this money left over, and Mom said there's no need to just let it lie around the house when she could be using that money, so she wants to cash it in.

"The teller took the bag I handed to her and began counting the bills. There were also some coins in the bag, but she put them back in and told me to tell my mom that they did not take coins. When she finished counting, she told me there would be about $82.00 left after the bank took their conversion fee. A few minutes later, I strutted out of the bank with $82.00 to spend on whatever I wanted. I headed straight for the mall and the arcade and played games until it was closing time.

"Three weeks later, I came home to an irate mother and a dad who threatened to beat my butt. Unbeknownst to me or to the teller who had taken the bills and given me the cash, that particular Belgium currency was no longer being accepted. Apparently, between the time my parents had returned from their trip and the time I tried to exchange the bills, Belgium had devalued their currency. Consequently, they had debited Mom's account for $51.00 to cover the amount they had given me for the now-devalued bills.

"After that, I really began getting into serious trouble. School was becoming a real pain, and I was getting thrown out of one school after another and was constantly ending up in either at Central or McLaren juvenile halls or Apple Valley Boys Ranch. McLaren wasn't so bad.

"In fact, I really didn't mind going there. Central, on the other hand, was a different story. Not only was it a much rougher crowd there, but it was rat- and roach-infested. One night after I had gone to bed, I just happened to peak out from under my covers, and the entire floor and walls looked like they were moving. Both were covered with roaches. I think that scared me more than the people who were locked up with me. From then on, I tried not to ever get sent back to Central.

"Anyway, it was in February of 1986, and I had been sent home from Apple Valley Ranch on a sixty-day home visit to try to get me acclimated back into my home. Mom and Dad weren't getting along too well at this point, and Grandma was really sick.

"The house felt different from the way it used to feel. For whatever reason, I just didn't feel like I belonged there anymore and was really depressed. I wanted to feel like I belonged. So, to get their attention, that night, I took Dad's car keys off the kitchen counter where he had laid them, went and opened the garage door, got into his car, and backed it out.

"Since we lived on a busy street, I was trying to judge when I could back the car out into the street without getting hit by an oncoming car. When I thought it was clear enough for me to make it, I hit the accelerator but lost control and ended up crashing his car into the wall of the church parking lot across the street. By the way, that was the same wall I had crashed into when I stole the neighbor's new Schwinn bike.

"Mom and Dad's reaction to me crashing Dad's car only made things worse for me. So, two days later, I went into

Grandma's room, got two bottles of her medicine, went into the kitchen, and swallowed somewhere around sixty pills. Within minutes, I began screaming and calling for help. Lynn ran in, saw the empty pill bottles, and immediately called 9-1-1.

"I was rushed to Whitehurst Hospital and Medical Center where they pumped my stomach and held me overnight for observation. From there, I was transported to the psychiatric unit at Children's Hospital in Los Angeles. I was held there from February 14th until March 6th.

"It's kind of ironic that we are discussing this matter now, because a couple of weeks ago, I was cleaning out a drawer with some old papers in it and found an evaluation paper completed by one of the clinical psychologists during that time. In fact, let me see if I can remember where I put it and get it for you when we get home."

Later that evening and true to his word, Dad found the paper and handed it to me. It read as follows:

To: Superior Court, County of Los Angeles
Juvenile Court
Date: March 6, 1986
Re: Terrance James Ferguson
Reference # 1387256
This 14-year-old child was admitted to Children's
Hospital on 2-14-86 as a result of a suicide attempt
while on a 60-day visit with his parents Dave and
Beetrice Ferguson.

• He ingested approximately 50 to 100 pills and was

sent to an emergency room before being placed in the Psychiatric Unit at Children's Hospital.

• I have met with both parents on several occasions and continue to meet with them on a weekly basis. I have also met and continue to talk with Marlene Jefferson of the Child Advocate office as well as Mr. Williamson of the D.P.S.S.

• After an extensive set of interviews with TJ, as well as an analysis of his psychological assessment, I have no doubt that this youngster is in need of a structured therapeutic program that will correct his severe impulsive behavior. This has been exhibited in such behavior as running away, truancy, stealing, destruction of property, and most recently, self- destructive behavior toward himself.

• This child needs to be placed in a setting in which he can also be rewarded for positive behavior which includes a strong emphasis on school achievement, as well as mature ways to express his anger.

• While in the program at Children's Hospital, he has started to make some positive steps. However, in the last week, he has begun to manipulate the staff. Since he has an attorney appointed by the court, he thinks he can tell the staff that he no longer wishes to be in the program if they make him follow rules.

• When asked where he would like to go if he left the Children's Hospital program, he states, 'I want to go back to the hall since the rules there are easier, and there are more girls there.'

• Also, when this youngster gets upset with the staff, he tells them, 'I don't have to follow the rules like all the other kids because the judge will let me do whatever I want.'

• I feel TJ needs to remain at Children's Hospital where he can get the help he needs. If any other placement is considered, it must be in a facility that is equipped to handle a youngster who continues to exhibit suicidal tendencies.

• My long-term goal in this case is family unification. I see both parents as cooperative and willing to achieve this goal and will continue to base my treatment plan with this objective as top priority.

• This youngster badly needs stability, so I am hoping this will work.

EIGHTEEN

Beginning of the End

F ollowing a few moments of reflection as I turned a page to continue making notes, TJ resumed his reflections.

"Unfortunately, Michael, things did not get better but instead continued to go downhill from there. One week after I was released from the Children's Hospital program, I had reoffended and this time was sent to Antelope Valley Boys Ranch. That was probably the beginning of the end. What I mean is that the trouble I had gotten in to up to this point was small-time stuff compared to where I was now headed. I hadn't been at Apple Valley two days before I got hooked up with this dude Chris who was a true dyed-in-the-wool gang-banger. He told me that things were pretty relaxed around the farm, and that it was easy to slip out at night without getting caught. That was music to my ears.

"A little over a month after I arrived, I decided to skip out again one night. However, this night was different. A few minutes after I snuck away from the ranch, I was walking down the street when I just happened to look down and lying in the middle of the sidewalk was a key. I picked it up and realized it was somebody's car key.

"It was about one in the morning, and the street was completely deserted. I decided I would try to find the car that the key belonged to and take it for a spin. It took over an hour of trying car after car until I finally found one that opened. The car looked like it was black, although it was hard to tell in the dark.

"The interior was pretty nice, and I think it was a Pontiac. I had put the key in the ignition and was getting ready to start it up when something told me to check the trunk. I got out, unlocked the trunk, raised the trunk lid, and knew I had hit the motherlode. I stood there staring at a 9mm Beretta semi-automatic, a pump-action shot gun, and a Winchester rifle. I could not believe my eyes. My hands were shaking as I got back in, started the engine, and took off heading back toward the ranch. Somehow, I had to get to Chris, show him what was in the trunk, and find out what I should do.

"Ten minutes later after sneaking back into the ranch, waking Chris up, and sneaking back out, we were standing there staring down at the guns. Chris really got excited and started rubbing his hands together and saying, 'TJ, man, we gotta git this stuff to the OG 'cause I know he's gonna want to have these.'

"Who?" I asked.

"'Man, you don't know nothin'!' Chris responded impatiently. 'The O! G! The Original Gangsta!' he said as he stomped and threw up his hands.

"As we got into the car, Chris got behind the wheel and took off heading toward LA. An hour or so later, we pulled up in front of a house in south central, and Chris got out and went up to the door and knocked. By this time, it was pretty close to three in the morning, but the lights were on in the house.

"The door opened, and after a couple of minutes, this huge dude came out to the car and headed straight for the trunk. Chris opened the door on the driver's side, took the key out of the ignition, and went back and opened the trunk. I didn't know whether to get out or stay put, but after another few minutes, the guy headed back into the house while Chris came around to the window and told me Doc Q wanted me to come inside. I hopped out and followed Chris up the steps and into the house.

"The place was a mess, and there was stuff everywhere. There were two women hanging out on the couch and a guy standing over in the corner by a table with drug paraphernalia on it. Chris and this dude headed straight for the back room. Once there, Chris told Doc Q, 'This here is TJ. He's the one who found the key and the car with the firearms in it.'

"Doc Q walked over, slapped me on the back, and said, 'Good job, TJ! Hey, I'm gonna give you guys a reward for bringing this stuff to me.' He then reached in his pocket, took out a wad of bills, peeled off a few, gave some to me, and some to Chris.

"Next, he said, 'Guys, I got something even better for you. Come on over here 'cause I got some rocks for you too. You can sell 'em and make you some more dough. All you gotta do is walk three blocks west from here, and your rocks'll be gone in ten minutes. Hey, Chris, you know I'm keeping the ride, don't you? You and yo' boy TJ gonna have to get your own transport back up the hill.'

"Once the supervisors at the ranch found Chris and me missing, they alerted law enforcement officers who staked out my house. Two days later when I showed up there, they immediately arrested me. Because I had committed the run-away offense in Los Angeles County, I was sent to Central again where there was no chance of me running away.

"Luckily, they never found out about the stolen car or the firearms."

NINETEEN

Back to the Nursing Home

During the drive home from the golf course after the long interview, I noticed that my dad was unusually quiet and appeared emotionally drained. There had been so much to share, and there would be one more chance to question my dad before I would have to catch my flight back to school. Later in the evening, long after my family had gone to bed, I sat looking at my notes from both Nanna and Dad, reflecting on how he would never in a million years have imagined the stories I was hearing.

I knew now that in pursuing this project, I had reopened old wounds: some that had never completely healed but had merely scabbed over, while others had remained open wounds that were still festering. I realized there was more to come as I had two more sessions to go with Nanna and at least one more session with Dad. I now prayed that at the end of this journey down a winding road filled with ruts, potholes, and forced detours resulting from avalanches, *somehow there would be a flower-filled meadow ... healing ... and peace.*

The next morning around ten, I headed back to Nanna's house, readied my recording device, and prepared for her to continue sharing where she had left off a couple of days before.

"After making the difficult decision to put Mother into a nursing home again, I began the search. Visits to several homes I had identified in my initial online search brought back images of Gilliam's, and I immediately deleted them from my short list. With only two homes left on the list, I paid a visit to Sierra Vista Nursing Home. It sat back about fifty feet from Olmstead Street in a quiet neighborhood located about a ten-minute drive from the high school where I taught.

"The home was surrounded by a sprawling lawn with numerous pine trees. Flower beds of multi-colored impatiens, wildflowers, and forget-me-nots along with numerous rose bushes provided a visual and fragrant feast. Benches were placed intermittently around the lawn. There were also a few patio tables and chairs for residents who wanted to enjoy sitting, conversing, having a bite, and being outdoors.

"The long, flat, gray building gave no hint to the warm and home-like atmosphere one would find inside. Much like the sprawling grounds, flowers played a major role in the décor, as vases were prominently placed throughout the reception area. There was no medicinal and urine odors as are usually found in many other nursing homes.

"The receptionist was friendly and courteous and exuded the same kind of warmth I would see later in the administrator and nursing staff. During the tour through the facility, I was allowed to go into a couple of rooms and briefly speak with a few of the residents. Although it was obvious that some were suffering from dementia or Alzheimer's, others were quite lucid and spoke highly of their experience at Sierra Vista. It was looking more and more like my search to find a good facility for Mother had come to an end.

"So, again with a heavy heart, I moved Mother into Sierra Vista on May 22, 1987. There were two beds in her room, but unlike the rooms at Gilliam's, these were much more spacious. There were larger closets and two large windows that made the room bright and sunny instead of the small one at Gilliam's that always made the room dark and dreary. I had taken time getting her all set up, clothes hung in her closet and put away in her drawers, and was reluctantly getting ready to leave so she could take a little nap before dinner. I had gone to get her a fresh water bottle and a glass.

"Just as I sat the glass on the table, she said, 'Baby, can you go in the kitchen and get me some of that good ole friend chicken you cooked last night?'

"My heart fell to the floor, and a knot formed in the pit of my stomach, for suddenly, it hit me that Mother would no longer be living with us and would probably never be able to live with us again. I ran from the room and into the guest restroom as tears spilled down my face.

"'Oh Lord,' I cried, 'I don't want to do this to my mother, but it looks like I have no other choice. She needs the kind of around-the-clock care that I can't provide for her now, and to deprive her of the medical attention and quick access to the help she needs would be abuse. But, Lord, it hurts so much. I don't want to leave her here, but I must. Help me to not to break down and cry in front of her and please help her to know that even though she is no longer living with me, I couldn't love her more.'

"Over the next six months, I developed a routine. Four times a week, either after school or during the weekends, I would stop at Paul's Grill and Deli and pick up six little bite-size coconut macaroon cookies to take to Mother. She loved those cookies almost as much as she loved Dairy Queen. I had to be careful, though, because she would eat every cookie in sight and then get sick. Six of those little cookies were just about the right sized serving.

"On the weekends, usually on Sundays, the nursing staff would have her ready when I got to the home, and we would go for a ride or to get her Dairy Queen treat. I remember once after Mother had been at the home for about a month, I got this bright idea to cook dinner and bring her to the house to eat and spend time with the kids.

"Big mistake! Once she got to the house, she refused to leave when it was time to take her back. In fact, she got up from the table, grabbed her cane, and trotted right on back to her room. When we tried to take her arm to steer her towards the front door, she pulled away, sat down in her rocking chair, refused to get up, and told us, 'You all are not taking me nowhere because I am not going back there!' It was only after she fell asleep sitting in her rocker that Dave went in, picked her up, and carried her out to the car. I learned a big lesson from that experience.

"The Sierra Vista staff began noticing that Mother would become noticeably reticent and withdrawn on the days when I was unable to visit. I felt badly, but I still had two children, or at least one when TJ was gone for whatever reason, that I needed to shuttle to doctor and dental appointments, after-school and church activities, and social functions.

"One month after moving Mother into the home, Lynn was in an accident and sustained head injuries. As a result, she not only had numerous doctors' appointments but was also on a home-study program that required a great deal of my attention. TJ, when he wasn't spending time in juvenile hall, also needed to be transported to his activities, and I definitely didn't want him feeling neglected again. Therefore, I had to take comfort in knowing that Mother was in a good facility where she was getting excellent care and medical treatment.

"On Friday, November 20th, I had stopped to pick up Mother's coconut macaroons and also a new baby blue sweater. On my previous visit, I had noticed it was starting to be a bit chilly in the recreation hall where she liked to sit in her wheelchair after lunch. The sweater would also give her a change from her favorite black one that was beginning to look like it had been through a couple of wars.

"When I arrived, she was sitting in the wheelchair in her usual spot near the piano. I think she loved sitting there to be able to enjoy the music and watch the different people who came in to play from time to time.

"When she saw me, the first thing she said was 'baby, you got my cookies?'

"I started teasing her and telling her that the only reason she was happy to see me was because I always brought cookies and had become just the 'cookie lady' to her. Then, I jokingly told her I had forgotten them, but when I saw her face drop, I pulled the bag out of my purse and handed it to her.

"While she was enjoying the cookies, I showed her the sweater, and she said she liked it. I don't know if she even saw the sweater since she was so busy eating her cookies. I laughingly told her I should have given her the sweater first because once she got her mouth on those cookies, getting her to pay attention to anything else was a lost cause.

"Looking back on that day, there was something so special about our time together. We laughed and talked as I combed her hair, then pulled a mirror out of my purse so she could see how pretty her hair looked.

"Many times after I had combed her hair, she would pat her head and laughingly say, 'Yeah, I remember when I used to comb your little nappy head. Now, you're combing mine.' There was not a sign of dementia anywhere. I spent about an hour there before telling her I had to run so I could get home and start preparing dinner for the family.

"That was the last time I saw her alive. On Sunday, November 22nd at 6:02 a.m., Mother passed away. I received the call at 6:25. My world seemed in shambles. How could she just up and die and leave me? For some strange reason, when I hung up the phone, I went straight to my purse, pulled out the comb I had used to comb her hair two days before, and just sat staring at the gray hairs still left between the teeth. It was the one tangible thing I had left of her. Tears started to flow like open faucets. Who was going to comfort me and give me advice and encouragement as I struggled with the seemingly million challenges hitting me from every angle?

"Surprisingly, the answer would come from the eulogy her pastor would give during her funeral."

TWENTY

Sophie's Funeral

"There we were again traveling the ribbon of Highway I-40 as it snaked east through Arizona, New Mexico, Northern Texas, and Oklahoma, on its way to Arkansas, our destination. Five years earlier, we had been on this same highway heading west with great expectations, happy that Mother was with us again, and looking forward to all the opportunities we hoped California would have to offer.

"There had been many high points and victories. Mother's health and the quality of her life had improved tremendously with a healthier diet, daily exercise, and reduced medication. Lynn had blossomed into a confident and mature eighteen-year-old woman. During high school, she had been active in Chamber Singers, show choir, and drill team. She had also organized a group of students who provided safe ride for other students needing a ride home after attending parties or social functions.

"Working with small children at Vacation Bible School

was probably her favorite summer activity. Dave's job, though stressful, had been all that he had hoped for and more. He still traveled, although not as much as in previous times, which meant that the daily running of the household still fell on my shoulders a great deal of the time.

"I had eventually found a choral director's position at a high school where the students were amazing and parents extremely supportive. We were attending a church in Whittier where I was also directing a youth choir. The time, money, and effort we had invested getting the house fixed up had been well worth it, and it turned out to be a spacious and comfortable home in a great neighborhood.

"On the other hand, we had faced more than our share of challenges. For TJ, the move had been just one more thing to add to his insecurity, and once we arrived in California, he began to manifest more and more symptoms related to child abuse.

"He seemed hell bent and bound on defying, disobeying, and deceiving. His constant run-ins with law enforcement and his resulting rapidly growing rap sheet were causes of much consternation. Compounding the stress was the exorbitant amount of money we were spending to cover his medical and mental health bills.

"Costs for replacing the property he damaged, items he stole, and payments made to cover his living expenses in the many detention centers and group homes continued to escalate. It was barely by the skin of his teeth that he had been released from his present detention facility and given permission to travel out of state to attend Mother's funeral.

"Lynn was still suffering from grand mal epileptic seizures

brought on by her head injury, and doctors were not having much success in regulating her medication so she could function normally. Then, there was the issue of our marriage barely hanging together by a slender thread. To make matters worse, for the first time in my twenty-four-year teaching career, I had been written up by my department chairman for taking off from school to go and pick up my daughter whose car had broken down and was stranded on the side of the freeway.

"It didn't seem to matter to him that I had notified the office and gotten another teacher to cover my class during the forty minutes I was away. Now, here we were on the way to bury my mother. I felt like I was sinking into an abyss with darkness closing in all around.

"For as long as I could remember, Mother had always said she wanted to be buried next to Daddy. Even as I was growing up, the insurance man would come to our house on the first Tuesday of every month to collect the $1.50 premium to cover their burial plots at Haven of Rest Cemetery. Mother had even written instructions in the family Bible regarding her and Daddy's wishes about their funeral and burial when they passed away.

"Twenty years ago, I had followed those instructions after Daddy's death, and now I was repeating it for Mother. To honor her wishes, I had had her body shipped back home to Little Rock. She had requested that her funeral be held at Canaan Baptist Church, even though it had been over ten years since she had been able to attend services there. I had also placed a call to Canaan's Pastor, Reverend Keaton, and asked him to officiate and give the eulogy.

"We arrived in Little Rock around six in the evening on Thanksgiving Day and headed straight for my cousin Marguerite's home where we would be staying. She had dinner waiting for us, and though I had always enjoyed eating her cooking while growing up, I hardly ate a bite. It was like I was in a trance, hoping to snap out of it soon and get back to reality.

"Following a fitful night's sleep, I got up, dressed, and prepared for what I thought would be the most difficult day of my life. Looking back on it, the day turned out to be far different from what I had expected.

"As the family filed into the church for Mother's service, I was pleasantly surprised to see so many people in attendance. Not only were there a lot of church members who had worked along beside her in the kitchen, been in her Sunday school or Bible study classes, or sang in the choir with her, but also many people throughout Little Rock who had known her in one capacity or another.

"I can remember thinking, *Only someone who has touched the lives of so many and has left a lasting impression can draw this many people out to her funeral after having been gone for so many years.* Even more impressive was that people had taken time to come to a funeral on the biggest bargain-shopping day of the year.

"The order of service proceeded with an opening selection by the choir singing one of Mother's favorite songs, 'We've Come This Far by Faith.' I immediately had a flashback to when she used to sing, 'We've come this far by faith, leaning on the Lord, trusting in His holy word. He never failed me yet' while she was ironing or as we sat on the front porch peeling peaches or apples that she would later can to preserve them for the winter.

"Sometimes, I would even join in, and she would look at me lovingly and say, 'You sing that song real good, baby, and you need to learn how to play it on the piano too.' And I did.

"After the reading of scriptures from the Old and New Testaments, and remarks from relatives, pastors, church members, and others who had known her, it was time for another musical selection. Mother had wanted Miss Bernice to sing 'How Great Thou Art,' and even though she was now old and feeble and her once-powerful voice mellowed with age, she delivered a touching and heartfelt rendition. A flood of memories came rushing in, and I broke down, unable to stop the flood of tears. How was I ever going to make it without her?"

"Pastor Keaton's eulogy followed the song. He began:

We come this morning to celebrate the exceptional life of Sophia Elizabeth Knowles, better known to us as Sister Sophie. She was born on February 4, 1890, and passed away on November 22, 1987. Today, we gather for her home-going service, and even though we are sad and dealing with the void her passing has left in our lives, this will not be a mournful service.

We are going to celebrate, for there is so much to celebrate. Let's begin by celebrating her birth ninety-seven years ago. I believe she was an angel sent from heaven to live among us and enrich our lives. Celebrate the fact that she developed a relationship with Jesus Christ while she was still a young girl, and she allowed that relationship to develop and to guide her throughout those ninety-seven years. Celebrate the fact that even though she was deprived of getting a formal education while growing up, she didn't let her lack of having that education stop her from fulfilling her purpose in life.

Celebrate that her faith was so strong that she didn't listen when folks told her there was no hope, no way of solving the problem, or that something couldn't be done. She just prayed for help and guidance and kept moving. Beetrice, celebrate the fact that after your mother's tragic death, Sister Sophie had the courage to take you without permission to seek immediate medical help.

Being the strong woman that she was, when the doctors told her there was no hope, she got on her knees and demonstrated that, 'Oh yes, with my God, there is always hope.' Celebrate the fact that she didn't let all the negative effects of your poisoning and the challenges you faced in early childhood stop her from seeking ways to help you get well and healthy and become the best you could possibly become. Beetrice, celebrate that she recognized your musical talent when you were very young and made every effort, even down to staying up all night washing and ironing other people's clothes, to get the money to give you for lessons.

. . .

Celebrate that even though she didn't learn how to read and write until she was an adult, she still knew the value of getting a good education and made sure that you, young lady, went to college. Celebrate the fact that she loved taking care of others and helping them succeed, and hopefully, all of you family members, and the rest of you here, are following in her foot-steps. Celebrate that she understood the power of prayer and unconditional love, and many of you are sitting her today because of it. Hopefully, this, too, has been passed on to her family.

Celebrate that she didn't let anyone or anything stand in her way when she set her mind to do something. She didn't care anything about expert opinions. When you'd try to win an argument with Sister Sophie by telling her that so-and-so, who had a degree from this place or that, had said this or recom-mended a certain way to do something, she would come back with, 'Honey, there are a whole lot of educated fools out there. They've got lots of book learning but ain't got a lick 'o common sense, so you can't say they're always right. I depend on God and the good common sense He gave me because He's got more sense than all of the experts.'

Let's celebrate that she lived the kind of life all of us should aspire to live. Celebrate that she lived such a fruitful and productive life, and that years after she moved away from

Little Rock, people remember her and appreciate the impact she had on their lives. The attendance here today at her funeral is a testament to that.

Celebrate the fact that you, Miss Beetrice, and you, too, Mr. Dave, did not neglect her in her old age but bent over backwards to make her life full, happy, and comfortable right up to the end. That, too, is a testament to how she raised you and the values she instilled in you. You certainly showed her, and the world, how you 'honor your father and your mother, that your days may be long upon the earth.'

On that same note, celebrate that you didn't hide her away somewhere and forget about her but instead took her into your home and bestowed upon her the kind of love and care she had bestowed on you years ago. Celebrate that God allowed her to live to the ripe old age of ninety-seven and be able to see the fruits of her labor.' Beetrice, she was blessed to see that little sickly and half-dead baby she carried around on a pillow for months, grow up to be healthy, graduate from college, become a woman of God, and an award-winning teacher and musician.

You and Dave also blessed her with grandchildren whom she adored and who brightened her latter years. Sister Sophie was placed on this earth to do a job, and from what I am able to observe today by looking at you, Beetrice, and knowing from whence you came, I'd say she did a bang-up job!

In conclusion, I'm going to ask you to do something that is unusual for a funeral or a home-going service. Whenever you go to the theater or attend a concert and see or hear an outstanding performance, you give the cast or performers a standing ovation. So, I'm going to ask you all to stand to your feet, and let's celebrate Sister Sophie's incredible life performance and the legacy she leaves by giving her a standing ovation.

"I remember the thunderous applause that went on for what seemed like several minutes, and at that moment, my focus changed completely. It was no longer about my loss but about my thankfulness that God, after the death of my mother Neiomi, had allowed me to be raised by such an incredible woman.

"Additionally, He had given me forty-six of those precious ninety-seven years she had lived on this earth. Pastor Keaton's eulogy had also stressed the importance of living your life in such a way that it positively touches and improves the lives of others. This was the legacy that my Muh Dear had left, and I needed to be about the business of following in her footsteps and creating a similar legacy.

"During the three-day drive back to California, I had time to reflect over and over again on Pastor Keaton's words. Surprisingly, I found great comfort in them. Yes, it hurt, and the loss was tremendous. Yet there was a peace in my spirit that I could not explain. There was one phrase that kept replaying over and over again in my head: 'Sister Sophie was placed on this earth to do a job, and from what I can see, she did a bang up one.' I couldn't help but smile.

"He was right: 'Let's celebrate!'"

TWENTY-ONE

The Priceless Gift

"Y ou know, Michael, twenty days after burying my mother, I received a gift that was and still is one of the best gifts I've ever received. The only word I can think of to describe it is PRICELESS. As a way of helping me cope and ease my grief after Mother's death, some of my choir students and their parents wrote and collected letters and pictures and created a scrapbook. They presented me with this gift during our Christmas party, which I had dreaded attending due to the raw emotions I was still dealing with, especially since Mother used to attend my Christmas concerts. Nevertheless, I decided to go anyway for the sake of the students.

"I can remember the moment like it was yesterday. Toward the end of the party, the parent who had come up with the idea and who was responsible for putting everything together asked me to come up and sit in a chair that had been placed at the front of the room.

"Once I was seated, Mrs. Brown proceeded to give an

introductory speech. In fact, I was so touched by her speech that later I had her write it down for me. It is on the first page of the scrapbook. Now that I think about it, let me go get the scrapbook so I can read the speech to you:

Mrs. Ferguson, we, the parents, along with your present choir students and some of your former students from Chicago, want to make this presentation to you this evening. We know that the last few months have been extremely difficult for you, especially with your mother's passing last month.

During the four years my sons have been involved in your choral program, I have been amazed at how you have been able to juggle and keep all the balls in the air. We have all watched how you have persevered and how you continue to meet each challenge with a never-give-up spirit.

What a role model you have been! It has not only encouraged me but many of your other parents and of course your students. We don't know everything related to your many struggles because you've managed to keep much of it to yourself. However, it is not too difficult to put two and two together when we hear our children coming home telling us about the phone calls you're constantly getting related to problems with your mother, your son, and your daughter after her accident and her severe head injury.

· · ·

We do know about some of the days you've had to take off to take care of some issues involving them, the times you've had to leave school to rush to the hospital to see about your mother, or you needing to run to your son's school to resolve an issue. In spite of all that, you have been there for me, helping with my boys and intervening when they run into problems here at school. Lord knows, after their dad left and I became a single parent, I don't know how I could have made it without your help.

You are always encouraging them and showing love and patience as you've tried to help them navigate through their teenage challenges. I know you're going through a difficult time right now, so I pray this little token will bring some comfort and show you how much we love you. Therefore, please accept this scrapbook given with love and appreciation for all you have done and continue to do.

"Michael, I sat there with tears streaming down my face as I accepted their precious gift," Nanna continued. "They were trying to take pictures, and I was trying to hide my smeared-makeup face from the cameras. One of the reasons I want to share the scrapbook with you is to show you just how much we impact other people's lives with what we say and do, even when we don't realize it. It can have either a positive or a negative effect. I'll let you take it with you tonight, and you can take your time going through it. Of course, I'll want it back before you leave and return to school."

"Of course, Nanna," he responded.

Two days later, Michael returned the scrapbook. "Nanna," he began, "that scrapbook is unbelievable, and now I know why it is so special to you. Not only were the letters insightful in terms of what you have done as a teacher, but it also shows how you helped some of your students overcome their problems as you were trying to help my dad overcome his. Wow, I never realized how one person can impact and change so many lives. Mrs. Brown's introduction and three letters in particular stood out and spoke to me. I made copies of them to keep, if that's okay with you."

"Sure that's fine," Nanna responded, "but I'm curious to know which ones you've chosen and why."

"Okay, why don't I read them to you so you'll have some idea why I chose them? The first one is from one of your Chicago students named Charles Bailey:

Hello Miss Bee,

I know you will be shocked when you see my letter since it has been over ten years since you taught me. Somehow, one of your choir parents from Walnut Ranch High School where you are presently teaching was able to locate me here in Chicago. Apparently, she got my name from our Madrigal Group's award certificate that is hanging in your choir room office and was able to track me down that way. After she explained what your parents and students in California were doing, I happily agreed to write and send the letter for your scrapbook.

. . .

I have always believed that people come into your life for a reason. Some are like the breeze that touches you briefly on a summer's day and moves on, while others are like the roots of a mighty oak tree planted firmly in your soul.

Miss Bee, you were and are my oak tree.

I don't know if you remember or not, but I first met you when I was a junior at William H. George High School in Chicago. My mother, sister, and I had just recently moved to Chicago from Mississippi, and I was totally lost in such a new and different environment. I had never known my father, and since my mother was gone most of the time working two jobs to provide for us, my sister and I didn't have much adult guidance.

Initially when I came to school to register, I signed up for choir because I thought it would be an easy class that would not require much work. Little did I know that it would be the class that would change my life. During the first week, I quickly learned that you were a no-nonsense teacher but also that you genuinely cared about your students. Wow, I soon realized that I had better get my act together, and I did so out of respect for you.

. . .

The first few weeks were hard. George High School was located in the middle of a park, and there were drugs, shootings, and gang activity going on all the time in that area. Therefore, I was forced to find alternative routes to get to school and back home in order to avoid these activities. However, your class made it worth the effort of getting to school. You had an unorthodox way of teaching, and you taught with passion and heart. Your demand for excellence and discipline is still paying off. This is quite evident now that I am out in the corporate world and working to support a family. Not only did you build on my mother's values and beliefs, but you enhanced them. Since many of my friends and I did not have fathers to teach us a man's role in life, you provided opportunities for us to be around men who acted as mentors and positive role models for us. It seemed like you understood what it was like to not have a father. You also gave us opportunities to see what the world was like beyond the school and our community. As a result, many of us have been able to go out into the world and make substantial contributions to society.

I regret having to write this letter at a time when you are suffering the loss of your mother, but I hope that sharing my feelings and expressions of gratitude will help ease your pain and bring a smile to your face. My wife sends her love and wants to thank you also for helping me become the man I am today.

. . .

If there is anything I can do now or in the future, please don't hesitate to call. My address and phone number are located at the bottom of this letter.

Sincerely,

Charles Bailey

"The second letter is not from a student but rather from Mrs. Rebecca Young, the mother of Jason Alexander from Walnut Ranch High School:

Dear Mrs. Ferguson,

I have admired you from afar since Jason joined your beginner's chorus three years ago, and I've watched you juggle teaching classes, directing choirs, taking students to Europe, taking care of your husband, children, and your elderly mother.

However, it was the night of your spring concert this past April that brought everything front and center for me. Midway the concert, you had your mother wave her hand and be recognized. Apparently she had been quite ill after suffering a stroke, and you were so proud that she had been able to attend the concert that evening. The speech you made while dedicating the song, 'Wind Beneath My Wings' to her was truly heartfelt. However, the high point came when you came down from the stage, knelt before your mother, and took her hand.

You then asked the audience to join you by turning to a family member or friend, taking their hand, and joining you and the choir in singing the chorus … 'Did you ever know that you're my hero and everything I would like to be?' At the conclusion, there was not a dry eye in the house. In fact, I think the Kleenex tissue stock rose to new heights that evening because so many of us simply could not stop the flow of tears. It was truly an emotional and memorable moment that will long be remembered.

I, too, have a mother who is suffering the devastating effects of dementia. As her caretaker, there are times when I feel so exasperated and exhausted that I can hardly put one foot in front of the other. Other times, my heart just aches as I watch the beautiful, healthy, vibrant woman who brought me into this world struggle to do simple and basic tasks or recall things or words that should be flowing out of her mouth effortlessly.

I am heartbroken when she accuses me or my children of stealing her money or locking up the food so she will starve to death. Many times, my patience wears thin, and I become agitated with my situation, even resorting to the 'Why me?' mentality. Then to add insult to injury, after I've lost my temper and gotten angry with her, I can hardly stand myself. The guilt I feel settles in and my mood indicator moves from angry red into the blue depression zone. It's a vicious cycle.

Even though you didn't share a lot with me about your mother, I sensed what you were going through. I've caught bits and pieces from what Jason has told me about you having to leave in the middle of class to rush home or to the hospital.

One incident in particular stands out in my mind. Apparently, the in-home nurse fell asleep, and your mom left the house and was found wandering out in the middle of a busy intersection in her nightgown. It's obvious it has not been easy. Yet it was so uplifting to see the love you showed and the patience you had for your mother in spite of all the challenges. I can't begin to tell you how that has encouraged me during some very dark days when all I wanted to do was crawl into bed and hug my pillow as tightly as possible.

I grieve with you on your mother's death, but I also thank you for showing me how to lovingly make it through some of the most difficult times a family can face. Now, I don't feel so isolated and alone. As you so famously say, 'Take one day at a time and enjoy every precious moment and try to always see things as blessings rather than curses.' Thank you for being that light of hope and warmth of comfort to those fighting to get through life's cold dark tunnels.

With love and eternal gratitude,

Rebecca Young, Mother of Jason Alexander

"Nanna, all the letters were powerful, but the one that was gut-wrenching for me was the one from Mary Jetson:

Dear Ms. Bee,

I can't believe it's been seven years since I last saw you. Victor told me about your mother passing away, and I am so sorry for your loss. He said that someone in California had contacted him, asking if some of your former students would be willing to write letters of condolences and encouragement for a book they were putting together for you. I immediately said I would gladly do so because you came into my life when I was at the lowest point I could possibly go and would probably be dead now if it hadn't been for you.

I remember the first day I walked into your choir class. You were standing there with this big smile on your face, welcoming us to what you said would be one of the most fantastic years of your time spent in high school. I was thinking to myself, *Yeah, sure, you are one crazy and delusional woman if you think this going to be a fantastic year for ME.* Well, as it turned out, it was better than fantastic. It was PIVOTAL!

I'm sure you remember what I share with you mid-way through that year after you invited me into your office. Apparently, you noticed that I had been crying during class, even though I thought I was doing it in such a way that no one would notice. There was no way in the world I had planned to divulge to you what I was going through at home. Yet being around you made me feel comfortable and loved, and I felt that if anyone would understand, you would. It wasn't like you were being nosey or anything, but for the first time in my life, it seemed like I had met someone who really cared about me and what I was going through.

It was even stranger when you shared with me that you had adopted a son, that he had been traumatized and abused, and had gone through a lot before you all adopted him. In fact, you said that was one of the reasons you fell in love with him when you all first met him. It was obvious he was trying to protect himself when he scrunched his face into this mean look and balled up his little fists, even at three years old. You and your husband wanted to take him and try to help mitigate the effects of all the abuse he had suffered. Looking back on it now, I certainly hope you have been able to accomplish that, and your son is blossoming into a healthy and well-adjusted teenager. Interestingly enough, sharing that information about your son showed me your true heart.

That's why I willingly came into your office that day, which was three days after I turned eighteen. The day after my birthday, my mother told me I had until the weekend to get out of her house.

She basically told me I was grown now and that she was no longer responsible for taking care of me. I know it was her boyfriend that told her to do that because he was mad that I told him he was no longer going to molest me and get away with it. You probably didn't know that I had turned eighteen because most students have already graduated by then.

However, during my second year of high school, I missed so many days that I didn't have enough credits to move on, and that threw me behind. That was the year I was suffering from depression due to the fact that I had been abused and molested for years, and my mother did nothing to stop the abuse. Since I didn't trust talking about it or sharing it with anyone else, I just bottled it up inside and kept it to myself. But when you came along, I felt I could talk to you about it and that you would listen, understand, and possibly help me.

. . .

I still remember that Friday you showed up at my house and how you helped me pack, then took me to the bus station and paid for my ticket so I could go to live with my aunt and uncle. Even though that arrangement didn't work out and I eventually had to return to Chicago and depend on you helping me some more, your being there for me saved my life. After you helped me get a job working at the community center and a room to rent at the Cunningham's, I eventually finished my senior year of high school by attending night school.

By then, you had already moved to California, and I lost contact with you. I had also admired your strong faith and how you went about quietly demonstrating that faith without trying to shove it down anyone's throat. I think you will be happy to know that I chose to attend theology school after graduation, and now I am an assistant pastor in charge of Women's Ministry at a large church in Detroit. How can I ever thank you enough for loving and caring enough about me to point me in the direction I needed to go? As a result, I have been able to help many other women in crisis through my outreach ministry. After hearing my story, it gives them some hope and direction in their lives.

As you grieve the death of your mother, I pray you take comfort in knowing that the things she instilled in you, you have used to help change and save the lives of others.

. . .

I love you, Ms. Bee!! May God continue to Bless you always.

Sincerely,

Mary Jetson-Wilson

"You know, Nanna," Michael reflected, "I think this letter packs the strongest punch for me because of what Mary had to go through and overcome. Many of the letters I read gave insight into what it's like for kids to grow up in single parent homes and in environments totally different from what my siblings and I experienced and to try to overcome the devastating effects of child abuse."

"It's funny you should say that, Michael," Nanna interjected, "because out of all the letters, this one also impacted me the most. I was at a point where I was so close to giving up on your dad, even though I would have regretted it for the rest of my life. Isn't it odd that one of my former student's success in overcoming all the abuse and the numerous problems resulting from that abuse would be the encouragement I needed to continue on with your dad?

"Surprisingly, though, that letter as well as the others in the book that were intended to be encouraging and uplifting ended up having a different effect. Once the euphoria of receiving the scrapbook wore off, stark reality hit me square in the face as questions began to arise. Reading testimony after testimony about how I had helped so many others overcome their challenges and move on to live highly productive lives, why then was my own son running amuck and his life becoming a total train wreck?

"Why was my marriage falling apart? Was my daughter feeling lost in all the goings-on as she struggled to overcome the devastating effects of her head injury? I had always had this strong desire to help others, but was I spending too much time dealing with issues outside my home and not paying enough attention to what was going on inside my home? Was this a way of subconsciously avoiding having to deal with issues at home that at times seemed overwhelming? Were things completely out of balance?

"Growing up, I had been taught that the order of your priorities should be God first, family second, other things after that. Were my priorities in the wrong order? These were questions that I needed to pray about, give serious thought to, and seek to find some answers. So, in a way, the scrapbook was a priceless gift serving a dual purpose: giving accolades but also demanding accountability."

TWENTY-TWO

Compounded Felonies

"**B**y September of 1988, Lynn, TJ, and I had moved from Hacienda Heights to Upland, and I enrolled him in Upland High School. Grandpa Dave and I were separated at this time but were attending marriage counseling sessions and still very actively co-parenting. Since I was told Upland had an excellent football program, we felt this would be a great carrot to dangle in front of TJ and encourage him to attend school."

"He had recently been released from his detention stay at Central Juvenile Hall, which was by far the worst experience he had had up to this point. We were hoping he would realize that spending time in juvenile halls was no picnic, no way to grow up, and would act as a deterrent. We were trying to convince him that he was missing all the fun of being a teenager. Also, as he got older and committed more serious acts, he was running the risk of ending up in adult court and being tried as an adult. Hopefully, he would take heed and listen.

"The school year started out on a bright note. Coach Wilson had observed TJ during football tryouts. He was excited about his athletic ability and potential and could not stop talking about what an asset he would be to the team. During my back-to-school-night visit, Coach Wilson took more time than he probably should have explaining his plans for TJ.

"He had not played football during his freshman year because most of that year was spent in juvenile halls. However, Coach Wilson felt he would easily qualify to make the varsity team once he got some playing experience under his belt. He was even talking about the possibility of him getting a football scholarship.

"I felt more hopeful than I had in years and could not wait to sit in the stands and cheer during his games. Unfortunately, he only played a couple of games before getting injured, and by the time his injury healed, he had been placed on probation because of low grades and truancy.

"Two weeks after school started, I began getting calls from the attendance office stating that TJ had not shown up for school that day. *How could that be?* I thought. I picked up the phone and called the school secretary who verified that TJ had indeed been absent that day as well as two days prior. I explained to her that every morning on my way to work, I personally drove him to school and dropped him off. We later found out that as soon as I dropped him off, he would go in the front door, walk straight through the building and out the back door.

"Since it was not a closed-campus school, it was hard to monitor who came and went. His first progress report, which came in the mail, indicated TJ had been absent twelve days, tardy three, and had an F grade in all subjects except football where he had a D. The floor was falling out from beneath us again.

"TJ had become friends with a student at Upland named Rickey, and unlike me, his mother was a stay-at-home mom. We actually had met at back-to-school night and spoke briefly about the challenges of raising teenage boys. Sometime around early October, TJ came to me and said he wanted to go and stay at Rickey's house, and his mother could drive them to school every day.

"I gave considerable thought to the request, then picked up the phone and called Rickey's mother, Helen. She basically substantiated what TJ had shared with me. She was concerned that he was prone to get into trouble between the time he got out of school and the time I got home from work.

"The arrangement would be that TJ would stay with Helen and Rickey during the week, and I would compensate her for the five days he was there. He would spend the weekends at home with us. It really would be a godsend and give me a little breathing room. It was also comforting to know that he wasn't just left to run the streets when I was not around. Again, I was hopeful and welcomed this new arrangement.

"Sometime during the day on Tuesday, November 15th, TJ managed to play hooky from school and came to our apartment. Since everyone was gone and he had no key, he broke through a window in Lynn's bedroom. Once in the house, he stole some jewelry from my room, food from the kitchen, and the extra key to Lynn's car.

"Since she had driven to her classes at California State University in San Bernardino, the car was not at the apartment. Helen had called as soon as I got home from work to ask if TJ was at the apartment. Apparently, he had missed all his classes that day, even though she had dropped both boys at school that morning. He was nowhere to be seen when she had gone to pick them up and still had not shown up prior to her calling.

"I informed her that there were indications he had been at the apartment and had taken some food. I did not mention the jewelry and at that time had no idea that he had also taken Lynn's extra car key.

"Around midnight, I thought I heard someone starting her car since her parking spot was close to my window. I jumped out of bed, peeked out the window, and just happened to catch a glimpse of her car's taillights as it turned the corner. I ran through the house screaming for Lynn to wake up because someone had stolen her car. Little did I know, it was the work of TJ until she happened to check her jewelry box and notice the spare key was missing.

"We immediately notified the local police as well as the California Highway Patrol. For the next thirty hours, we had no idea where TJ or the car might be. It wasn't until I received a phone call from the Green River Police Department in Utah around 2 a.m. stating that they had my son in custody that I knew where he was.

"According to the police, they had clocked a car going around sixty miles an hour, speeding through downtown

Green River and had pulled them over. The boy driving the car, Christian Walker, had no driver's license, and the underage passenger was my son, Terrance. A search of the car netted some rock cocaine and an unopened can of beer. The car had been impounded, Christian was arrested, and Terrance was being held in a juvenile detention hall.

"The officer also informed me that there were no registration papers found in the car, and that when they ran the license plate number, it matched a 1986 Buick that had been involved in an accident and was now listed as a demolished vehicle. This sounded to me like TJ and this Christian guy had probably gone to a junkyard and stolen plates from a wrecked car so as to avoid being caught by the highway patrol who would be looking for Lynn's license plate number. However, that would be confirmed later. Meanwhile, the officer gave me the name of a contact person whom I could call during regular business hours and get more detailed information.

"So, here we were again back at square one. No, let me rephrase that: we were back in cellblock one. How could any of us in this family ever move ahead when TJ just kept reoffending and reoffending? That boy had to have had the highest recidivism rate of anyone in the entire juvenile justice system. I waited until daybreak to call Dave and inform him of our latest TJ crisis.

"My call the next day to the supervising officer on duty basically got me nowhere. I was told that because it was the weekend, nothing could be done until Monday. Seems like TJ had a knack for committing offenses on Fridays and therefore ending up having to spend the entire weekend locked up until Monday when they could have a detention hearing.

"For some unknown reason, TJ's detention hearing was not held until that Tuesday. At the hearing, the judge said he was extraditing him back to California because there was an outstanding warrant for his arrest related to some other charges. Therefore, he was returning him to California via Greyhound® bus and that officers would be there to meet the bus when it arrived and take him into custody. I was told that I would have to make the trip to Green River to pick up Lynn's car.

"Thanksgiving Day is supposed to be the day you celebrate and thank God for all the blessings you have received, spend time with family and friends over turkey dinners with all the trimmings, watch football games nonstop, and relax after dinner, complaining about how much you ate. However, for Dave and me, it was the second year in a row that we were on the road traveling on Thanksgiving Day.

"Last year, we had been on Interstate 40 heading east to Little Rock, Arkansas, to bury Mother. This year, we were on a Greyhound bus heading north to Green River, Utah, to pick up Lynn's car. The fifteen-hour trip was no picnic, and the dried-out turkey and soggy dressing consumed at one of the Greyhound rest stops did little to make it feel like a day of celebration.

"We arrived in Green River around three in the morning and just decided to wait at the station until daylight. Our plans were to go to the police station, show our identification and car insurance papers with car description and VIN number, pay the storage fee, get the car from the impound lot, and be on our way back to California. Not so! Four hours after we entered the police station, we were still waiting for them to remove the invisible red tape they seemed to have strung around Lynn's little 1984 Nissan Sentra.

"There were two reasons why they were reluctant to release the car. First, as I had suspected, TJ and Chris had apparently stolen the license plate from a wrecked vehicle before leaving California. They had also either destroyed or thrown away the registration that Lynn always kept in her glove compartment. Luckily, Dave and I had brought along the paperwork we had gotten when we purchased the car as well as the insurance papers. At least our thinking ahead helped us clear the first hurdle. However, there was a bigger one waiting just around the corner.

"Second, and more importantly, drugs had been found in the vehicle, and therefore it had been impounded as 'a vehicle used to transport drugs or other contraband.' Even though we were called and told to make the trip to Utah to pick up the car, apparently because we arrived the day after Thanksgiving, the supervisor who had been given the paperwork regarding that particular car had taken the day off.

"So, there we sat while someone tried unsuccessfully for several hours to reach him. It was not until 1:00 that afternoon that we were finally able to pay the $285 impound fee and retrieve Lynn's car. Exhausted and totally frustrated, Dave and I headed back to California. Would this TJ-antics saga ever end?

"Meanwhile, we were under the impression that TJ was back in California, had been taken into custody, and was at the detention center awaiting the hearing regarding his outstanding warrants as well as the theft of Lynn's car. We had arrived back home around one in the morning on Saturday, and I was sleeping in a bit trying to recover from the past grueling thirty-eight hours.

"Somewhere around 8:00 a.m., I thought I heard a tapping on my bedroom window but figured it was just a tree branch banging up against it. I ignored it and turned over to go back to sleep, but after hearing it a second time, I peeked through the blinds and saw TJ standing there with a sheepish look on his face. I opened the window and told him to go around to the front so I could open the door. When he came into the house, I asked, 'What are you doing here? Aren't you supposed to be at the detention center?'

"For the next ten minutes, I sat mesmerized and could not believe what I was hearing. He began by telling me that he and Chris had been given a job by the OG to transport some drugs to Chicago. So, he played hooky from school after Helen dropped him off, broke into our apartment, stole his sister's extra car key, some of my jewelry for Chris to pawn, and some food so they could eat on the way.

"Later that night, they came back and took the car. They realized that we would notify the police and the California Highway Patrol, and they would easily be spotted, so they went to a junkyard and found a car that had been wrecked but had current plates and took one of the plates. They put the new plate on the back and discarded both the front and back plates on Lynn's car. Next, they destroyed the copy of her registration.

"He and Chris had made it as far as Green River, Utah, when they realized they were running out of gas. Because it was early in the morning and the streets were deserted, Chris didn't realize he was speeding until the cop pulled him over.

Chris didn't have a driver's license, and they also found the drugs in the car, so they arrested him and took him to jail because he was eighteen. Because TJ was only fifteen, they sent him to detention center until Tuesday when the judge said they were extraditing him back to California because of an outstanding warrant.

"I then asked TJ, 'So, how are you able to be freely walking around like you are? They told me they were extraditing you back here, and that cops would be waiting for you when you arrived. So, what's going on?' I had come to associate TJ's slightly lopsided grin with deception, and that was not sitting well with me right now."

"'Well, you see, Mom," he began, 'when they put me on the bus in Utah, they told the bus driver to make sure I didn't get off the bus until we got to Pomona where the cops were supposed to meet the bus. However, when we changed bus drivers in Vegas, I figured the first driver must have forgotten to tell the new bus driver.

"'So, once we got close to Pomona, I noticed that we weren't too far from our apartment. When we came off the freeway, we came to a stop at the end of the off ramp. I just asked the driver if he could pull over and let me off since I lived just down the street, and he said, "No problem." Since no one was home last night, I went to Rickey's place, climbed the fence to get into their backyard, and slept in the lawn chair until this morning.'

"When I finally found my voice and felt it was steady and calm enough for me to speak, I turned to him, looked him straight in the eye, and said, 'TJ, I've! Had! Enough! You will no longer commit your crimes and not suffer the consequences. You stole your sister's car and drove it to Utah. Thank God you all got caught or you would have been in Chicago, and we probably would never have found you or the car. The officers in Utah said you were extradited to California because there is a warrant for your arrest related to a totally different offense. Bottom line: you need to turn yourself in and face the consequences for what you have done. You can no longer stay here, and I'm going to make certain that you cannot stay at Helen's either. Your only option at this point is to go and turn yourself in. I'll be happy to drive you to the nearest police station.'

"Once we arrived, I wanted to make certain he turned himself in rather than just letting him out and he take off down the street. I parked the car and accompanied him into the station.

"When he gave his name to the officer at the front desk, the man almost jumped out of his chair. 'You're the kid who gave us the skip. We were at the Pomona bus station waiting for you, and when the bus pulled up, you were nowhere to be found. The driver told us he let you off at the Central Avenue exit and said he didn't have any instructions about making sure you didn't get off until you got here. We've had officers looking all over for you since yesterday.'

"He turned to me and asked, 'Are you his mother?' I answered I was, and that I wanted to make sure he turned himself in.

"Several days after TJ turned himself in, I received the following via certified mail:

. . .

To: TERRANCE JAMES FERGUSON; THE MINOR'S PARENTS, GUARDIAN OR OTHER RESPONSIBLE ADULT RELATIVES:

You are required to appear at the San Bernardino Juvenile Court on December 9, 1988, at 1:00 P.M. for a hearing on the following matters:

COUNT 1: On or about November 15, 1988, in the County of San Bernardino, State of California, the crime of USE OF A VEHICLE WITHOUT PERMISSION, in violation of PENAL CODE SECTION 499b, a Misdemeanor, was committed by said minor, TERRANCE JAMES FERGUSON, who did willfully and unlawfully, without the permission of the owner thereof, to wit, Lynn Ferguson, take a 1984 Nissan Sentra for the purpose of temporarily using and operating the same.

COUNT 2: On or about November 15, 1988, in the County of San Bernardino, State of California, the crime of UNLAWFUL DRIVING OR TAKING OF A VEHICLE, in violation of VEHICLE CODE SECTION 10851(a), a Felony was committed by said minor, TERRANCE JAMES FERGUSON, who did willfully and unlawfully drive and take a certain vehicle, to wit, a 1984 Nissan Sentra, license #KSA254, then and there the personal property of Lynn Ferguson without the consent of and with the intent, either permanently or temporarily, to deprive the said owner of title to and possession of said vehicle.

COUNT 3: On and between October 3, 1988, and October 4, 1988, in the County of San Bernardino, State of California, the crime of USE OF A VEHICLE WITHOUT PERMISSION, in violation of PENAL CODE SECTION 499b, a Misdemeanor was committed by the said minor, TERRANCE JAMES FERGUSON, who did willfully and unlawfully, without the permission of the owner thereof, to wit, Budget Rent A Car, take a 1988 Toyota Corolla for the purpose of temporarily using and operating the same.

COUNT 4: On and between October 3, 1988, in the County of San Bernardino, State of California, the crime of HIT-RUN DRIVING, in violation of VEHICLE CODE SECTION 20002(a), a Misdemeanor was committed by the said minor, TERRANCE JAMES FERGUSON, who was the driver of a vehicle involved in an accident resulting in damage to property, who did willfully and unlawfully fail, refuse, and neglect to leave in a conspicuous place on the vehicle and other property damaged, a written notice giving the name and address of the driver and of the owner of the vehicle involved, and a statement of the circumstances thereof and without unnecessary delay notify the Riverside Police Department of the place where the collision occurred.

.   .   .

NOTICE IS HEREBY GIVEN THAT THE PRIOR DISPOSI-
TIONS HAVE BEEN INEFFECTIVE AND/OR THE PETI-
TIONER INTENDS TO RELY ON ALL PRIOR OFFENSES
IN ORDER TO ENHANCE THE MAXIMUM PERIOD OF
PHYSICAL CONFINEMENT.

NOTICE IS HEREBY GIVEN TO THE PARENTS AND
ALL OTHER PERSONS AND ENTITIES LIABLE FOR
THE SUPPORT OF THE MINOR, THAT YOU ARE
LIABLE, JOINTLY AND SEVERALLY, FOR THE COST
OF: 1) PROBATION SUPERVISION; 2) CARE, SUPPORT,
AND MAINTENANCE IN ANY PLACE OF DETENTION
OR MAINTENANCE; 3) ANY ATTORNEY APPOINTED
BY THE COURT, FOR YOU OR THE MINOR. WELFARE
AND INSTITUTIONS CODE SECTION 903 AND
FOLLOWING minor is detained and was taken into custody
on November 26, 1988, at 110 Hours. THEREFORE, Peti-
tioner respectfully requests that this minor be adjudged and
declared a ward of the Juvenile Court, pursuant to the provi-
sions of Section 692 of the Welfare and Institutions Code of
California.

Thomas McNamara, District Attorney, Petitioner

TWENTY-THREE

The Hearing

"For the umpteenth time, Dave and I found ourselves entering a juvenile courtroom. This time, it was for TJ's dispositional hearing, which was being held in courtroom B at the Juvenile Courthouse in San Bernardino. We slid into the first row of chairs located directly behind where TJ and his attorney, Charles Blackman, would be sitting. I tried to calm my nerves and hide my shaking hands. Up to this point, the charges had been minor compared to what he was now facing. Lord only knew where he would end up after his sentencing today.

"Prior to today's hearing, TJ had admitted to the four counts listed in the petition. However, his attorney had been able to make a plea bargain with the district attorney to have counts one and three, use of a vehicle without permission, both misdemeanors, dropped. Count two, unlawful driving or taking of a vehicle, a felony, and count four, hit-and-run driving, a misdemeanor, remained.

"Just as the hearing was about to begin, Coach Wilson arrived and joined us, sitting in the empty chair we had saved for him next to Dave. In an effort to mitigate the severity of TJ's sentence, I had asked him to come and speak to the judge about TJ's athletic potential. Thankfully, he had agreed, even though it meant taking a half-day off from work. I had also planned to speak from a different viewpoint to provide information that I hoped would also be a mitigating factor.

"To help validate my claims, I had requested documents from both Dr. Sheldon and Dr. Moore's offices and had obtained certified copies of the psychological evaluation from Fitzgerald Hospital and documentation of observations made while TJ was at Children's Hospital. These documents, hopefully, would highlight the complex nature of the challenges he was facing. I had asked his attorney to see if he could have them admitted into evidence.

"Finally, we had hired Dr. Bernadine Archer, one of the leading child psychologists in southern California's Inland Empire, to testify as an expert witness. We felt her testimony would help Judge Riker understand the emotional and psychological challenges TJ was facing. Would any of this matter though or have an impact on his sentence?

"Dr. Archer was a soft-spoken woman, and at first, I wondered if we had made a mistake in hiring her. However, her soft-spoken and mild-mannered demeanor belied her knowledge and understanding of challenges abused and neglected children face. We could not have asked for a stronger or more passionate advocate for children who had come out of situations similar to TJ's. The empathy her testimony generated as she hit key points regarding the challenges someone in his position would face was evident as I watched Judge Riker's face and body language, and even the subtle, but visible reaction of the District Attorney.

"'Good morning, Your Honor. May it please the Court, my name is Dr. Bernadine Archer, and I presently head the Counseling and Mental Health Institute of the Inland Empire located in Loma Linda. I received a Master of Arts degree in Clinical Psychology with a specialization in child studies from Yale University in 1971, and for the past fourteen years, I have been a practicing child psychotherapist at the institute.

"'Today, I'd like to begin by painting a picture of a child with a background similar to the defendant, Terrance, also referred to as TJ. I'll call this child Mary. Mary was born to a mother who was addicted to drugs and immediately began manifesting signs of drug withdrawal. She began having tremors several hours after birth and cried excessively even after being changed and fed.

"'There were times when her crying was so high pitched that her cry could be distinguished from the cry of other babies in the nursery. Within the first two weeks, Mary also had several seizures. Because of her medical problems, she was kept in the hospital for an additional two-week period following her birth. Mary's mother was a single mother struggling with drug addiction, so Mary was taken away when she was only a month old and placed in the foster care system.

"'Unfortunately, in this case, the couple with whom Mary was placed had only become foster parents to supplement their income. She presented challenges the foster parents weren't prepared or willing to deal with, and she began to get on their nerves. This led to abuse in the form of putting Mary in a crib, closing the door, and just letting her cry until she was exhausted and finally fell asleep. They even refused to hold her but rather would prop a bottle up on towels, then have one of the other kids go into the room and turn her on her stomach to burp her.

"'Eventually, Mary was removed from that home when a CPS agent paid an unexpected visit and found Mary in deplorable condition. Her diaper was soaked and feces caked on her bottom which was evidence that she had not been changed in hours. The agent also found bed sores and what appeared to be bed bug bites. Mary was immediately removed and placed in a different home. However, dealing with the withdrawal problems was still a challenge. So, for the next few years, Mary lived in four different foster homes. The constant moving, the lack of stability which removed the opportunity for her to bond, the abuse and neglect she suffered as she moved from place to place began to manifest itself early.

"'At age four, Mary was finally adopted by Denise, a divorced mother who was looking for a sibling for her eight-year-old daughter, Melonie. Denise had been given a heads-up regarding Mary being born showing signs of drug addiction and the abuse she had suffered in the foster homes. She thought she was prepared to deal with those challenges.

"'A few days after the adoption, Denise noticed that Mary never smiled and was sullen and withdrawn most of the time. This was disconcerting since she and her daughter were doing everything possible to make her feel comfortable and at home.

"She also noticed that on two occasions, Mary had gone into Melonie's room, taken her dolls, stuffed animals, toys, and other belongings and either thrown them around the room or had mutilated the dolls and stuffed animals and also ripped her diary to shreds. Denise mentioned this to the pediatrician when she took Mary for her required checkup, and the pediatrician recommended Denise get in touch with a child psychologist immediately.

"Unfortunately, Mary's enrollment and participation in numerous mental health and psychotherapy programs over the next twelve years were not enough to eradicate all of the negative effects of the abuse and neglect. The maltreatment she had experienced during the first four years of her life continued to dominate and control her actions. As she moved further into her teens, her bizarre, disruptive, and erratic behavior seemed to escalate.

"She began using drugs at an early age and stole just about everything she could from her mother, sister, and anyone else she could to support her drug habit. She was expelled from several schools, refused to complete her home-schooling assignments, and ended up dropping out of all educational programs. She then began running away from home, and the last we heard, she had been picked up off the streets for the fifth time and placed in a group home. She remained there only a few days before running away again. Odds are slim that she will ever be able to get her life back on track.

"'I'm sure you're wondering, *How could Mary continue to behave in this manner since the abuse she experienced happened many years ago?* You're also probably questioning, *How could she do this to Denise and Melonie who had done everything humanly possible to help her recover from her negative experiences?* Well, the answers are not easy ones.

"'Let's begin with the impact of Mary's mother's drug use while pregnant. Studies conducted by the U.S. Department of Health and Human Services and the U. S. Department of Education found that one-half to three-quarters of a million infants born each year have been exposed to illicit drugs in utero. As a result, the children sustain permanent neurological, developmental, and behavioral consequences. They tend to lack social skills, have difficulty keeping pace with normal routines, are withdrawn, and display sudden episodes of violence. This would explain, in part, why Mary impulsively went into her sister's room and destroyed her dolls, stuffed animals, and her diary.

"'Now let's turn our attention to the other side of the picture, the negative impact of child maltreatment. According to publications by the Center for Behavioral Medicine, child maltreatment includes both abuse and neglect of a child and can occur in different forms. Physical abuse can include, but is not limited to, the perpetrators inflicting injury by hitting, biting, kicking, slapping, or burning.

"'It can also include using objects such as belts, sticks, rods, or bats. Neglect, on the other hand, can include everything from failure to meet their nutritional needs to ignoring or continually failing to respond to a child's crying or withholding touch or emotional engagement. They also found that abused children have serious problems with trust issues. Abuse by basic caregivers, the ones who are supposed to keep them safe and the ones they rely on to meet their basic physical and emotional needs, raises the questions that if you can't trust them, who can you trust?

"'All forms of abuse, be it physical, emotional, or psychological, leave scars that last throughout a lifetime. Mental health consequences of abuse can increase anxiety or depression, or the individuals may even attempt suicide. Another study done by the Center on the Family focused on the lasting effects of early infancy environments and the changes that the brain undergoes during that period. This study showed that the levels of stress hormones, cortisol, were much higher years after the abused child had been removed from that negative environment than those of children from non-abusive environments.

"'Other studies showed the children experiencing early childhood deprivation had different levels of oxytocin and vasopressin, hormones that are linked to emotional and social bonding. Their levels remained high despite the fact that these children had been relocated for three or more years into a loving, stable, and secure environment. Conclusions were that change in environment did not seem to have eradicated all of the negative effects of the abuse and neglect.

"'As these children grow up, they tend to have low self-esteem, become cold, uncaring, and indifferent, feel unworthy of love, seek constant approval, and create an emotional void. They also tend to rebel against anyone trying to supervise, guide, or counsel them. Many of them try in one way or another to inflict self-harm or commit suicide as we have seen with this defendant who, according to documents submitted from Children's Hospital, swallowed around 100 pills.

"'Dr. Jim Hopper, a nationally recognized expert on victims of child abuse, states that in 1975, during the time Terrance was in the foster care system in Chicago, child abuse was at an all-time high. The National Criminal Justice Reference Service states that there were over 91,000 Children in Illinois during the 1970s that were reported to have been abused or neglected. In the case of Terrance, three reports were filed by Illinois State Child Welfare agencies under the Illinois Abused and Neglected Child Reporting Act, confirming that he had been the victim of child maltreatment.

"'Finally, if we consider the negative impact of being born with a drug addiction problem, then layer on top of that the challenges presented by abuse and neglect, we now have some idea of what people like Mary and Terrance are facing daily. The studies I have cited paint a bleak picture for a large number of children. We can only hope that as the public is made more aware of the plight of these children, that we as a society will show more compassion and help develop programs that will address their mental and emotional health issues. Instead of adopting an attitude of simply punishing them, let's work toward finding solutions that will make it possible for them to live healthy, well-adjusted lives.

"'Thank you, Your Honor, for allowing me this opportunity to speak to the court.'

"Following Dr. Archer's testimony, there was a you-could-almost-hear-a pin-drop moment as Judge Riker continued making notes on his pad. Twice, before speaking, he looked up and over at TJ, then looked back at his pad as he made a few more notes. Finally, after what seemed like a lifetime, he looked up, thanked Dr. Archer for her testimony, before instructing Attorney Blackman to call his next witness.

"Coach Wilson was called to the podium to give his statement. 'Good morning, Judge Riker. May it please the court, my name is Wardlow Wilson, and I am the junior varsity coach at Upland High School. Terrance enrolled at the high school this past August and approached me about playing on the football team. It was two weeks before school would start, and we were preparing to play our first game at the end of the first week of school.

"'Even though Terrance had not participated in our summer football camp which is designed to hone the skills of our players, I told him to come out to the field that afternoon and try out. He had not been on the field ten minutes before I recognized that this kid was extremely talented and showed a natural ability that some of my seasoned players did not have.

"'During the two weeks prior to our first game, his natural ability to read and execute plays demonstrated skills that cannot be taught. In some instances, he was performing better than some of the players who had just returned from football camp. At that time, I was unaware of the emotional and psychological problems he was dealing with and was focusing instead on developing his raw talent to such a level that he would be prepared to play varsity next year.

"'I also wanted him to start attracting the attention of college recruiters and had even spoken to Mrs. Ferguson during back-to-school night regarding possible scholarship opportunities. Unfortunately, Terrance was only able to play in three games before getting injured. Once he recovered, his grades had dropped so low that he became ineligible to play with the team. I sincerely believe that if Terrance could be placed in a facility where he would be able to participate in a structured athletic program and develop that tremendous talent, he could turn his life around. Given the right set of circumstances, he might even go on to play college or professional ball.

"'He has unbelievable speed which he demonstrated during the short time he was on the field, so he probably would also do well in a track and field program. Judge Riker, I certainly hope you take these comments into consideration when placing Terrance. Thank you.'

"I was the last person to be called to the podium, and it was obvious that I was nervous, for as I began to speak, my voice trembled so much that I had to take a couple of deep breaths before I could continue. 'Good morning! May it please the court, I am Beetrice Ferguson, and I am here to speak on behalf of our son, Terrance James. My husband Dave and I adopted Terrance in June of 1976 when he was three-and-a half years old.

"'Prior to his adoption, Terrance had spent thirty-nine months in foster care after being taken away from his mother who was addicted to drugs. During those thirty-nine months, he was severely abused and neglected, some of it stemming I believe from the challenges of drug withdrawal that he was manifesting. There was physical evidence that he had been beaten, burned, and deprived of food. His emotional development was negatively impacted since little attention seemed to have been paid to his needs of being held, loved, and supported.

"'The fact that he was placed in four different homes during those thirty-nine months certainly underscores the problems he would later have with bonding and feeling secure. Referring back to Dr. Archer's earlier testimony, Terrance could certainly be considered a male version of Mary, whom she used to demonstrate the challenges faced by abused and neglected children.

"'As you can see from the documents Attorney Blackman has admitted into evidence, my husband and I have done everything humanly possible to help Terrance with family support, financial support, mental health assistance, athletic programs, social development opportunities, and anything else you can imagine. But again, referring back to something Dr. Archer stated, and I paraphrase, "Once kids have been abused early in life, they are still negatively impacted by that abuse years after they have been removed from the abusive environment."

"'Coach Wilson testified that Terrance is extremely talented and suggested that a structured program where his athletic skills could be honed might make a huge difference in his life. I agree. I believe that if we can put him in a structured program where a trained coach can continue to help him develop his talent, it will give him a different focus, help him build self-esteem, and prove his self-worth. Once he experiences success in one area, I think it will motivate him to want to achieve success in other areas.

"'Your Honor, it is obvious that placing him in the juvenile halls and group home settings here in southern California has not worked for many reasons. I feel Terrance is not motivated because there are no structured programs to help him focus on something other than just hanging out with his homeboys. As the old adage goes, "An idle mind is a devil's workshop." I think putting him someplace where he has to work toward meeting a goal, earning some credits, and developing his athletic skills would make a world of difference.

"'Your Honor, I pray you put him where he will begin developing the skills to realize his potential, where he can start to believe that he is somebody, and that he does not have to resort to doing negative and destructive things to be noticed and get attention. Similarly, he does not have to depend on the other guys in the gang to give him that pat on the back after he has gone out and fulfilled his mission in order to be accepted.

"'Please put him where he is treated like he has already accomplished his goals. One of my favorite songs has always been "Wind Beneath My Wings," and that's what I'm asking here today. That we become the wind beneath his wings by putting him in an environment where he can develop his talents and which will allow him to soar and reach incredible heights.

"'Thank you, Your Honor, for allowing me to share my thoughts this morning.'

"Twenty minutes later following a brief recess, Judge Riker returned to the bench and instructed Terrance and Attorney Blackman to stand.

"Judge Riker then began speaking. 'Terrance, you are lucky to be standing here today in front of me, and you're also lucky to have supporters like your parents and Coach Wilson who were willing to come here today and speak on your behalf. I have listened carefully and taken under advisement the things Dr. Archer, Coach Wilson, and your mother have shared. Their comments have factored greatly in my decision.

"'Before I continue with informing you of my decision, I'd like to ask you a couple of questions. I know this is not normal procedure, but I feel I can take the liberty of asking these questions. A yes or no answer is sufficient, and I don't need you to elaborate. First, do you realize that your time for committing offenses, getting a slap on the wrist, and being sent home with your parents is over?'

"Terrance immediately responded, 'Yes, sir, Your Honor!'

"'Second, do you know that most young people that come into my court do not have the kind of support that I've seen demonstrated here today, and that you are lucky to have parents who have spent thousands of dollars to help you and people like Coach Wilson giving up his time to come in here and speak on your behalf?'

"'Yes sir, Your Honor!' Terrance again responded.

"'I want you to hear me and hear me clearly, young man. The only reason I am making the decision to send you to the place where I am sending you is because, thanks to Dr. Archer, I now have a better understanding of the battles you are fighting everyday due to the challenges you have been faced with since birth. It is unfortunate that so many of our children are born with strikes against them.

"'For you to have to go through something as traumatic as drug withdrawal as a newborn, then fight the effects of abuse and neglect is beyond my comprehension. It was also sobering to hear that you are probably still being impacted by the negative effects of that abusive environment, even though you've been out of it for about twelve years.

"'Coach Wilson spoke about your natural athletic ability and seems to feel that developing that talent might be the catalyst for turning your life around. Our goal here is not to lock you up for the sake of locking you up but to put you in an environment that will help you change your negative habits and enable you to find positive and socially acceptable ways to get what you need and want.

"'Another goal is to help you learn skills that will allow you to adequately support yourself, become a viable citizen, and lead a full and productive life as opposed to just being a burden on the state as an inmate. Therefore, tomorrow you will be traveling to northern Nevada, where I am placing you in a nine-month program at the Athletic Training Center. I'll warn you right off the bat, it is a challenging program and at times will push you to your limit.

"'However, if you stick with it, earn your credits, and do what you're told, you could return to southern California a changed young man. There are good coaches at the training center, so you'll have opportunities to develop your talents, learn skills that could be beneficial, and possibly compete in some of the local competitions. Remember, though, Terrance, this is your last chance.

"'If you continue down the path you've chosen up to this point, then you are looking at a lifetime of being locked up, having no freedom, wasting your talents, and never being able to lead a normal life. So, take heed, and I hope I never see you back here in my courtroom again, which will be a good thing. I wish you the best!'"

TWENTY-FOUR

The Turning Point

Michael was almost finished with his job of interviewing family members and delving into the anecdotal material provided during the sessions. However, he still needed to have one more round with his dad. The first interview had gone well. However, after having been out in the sun playing the eighteen holes, both were low on energy and ran out of steam before covering a lot of what he still wanted to cover. Now, he was running out of time and had to get this done today because he was due back at school on Monday.

Since it was the weekend, everyone had taken off to run errands, go shopping, and attend dance class, so the house was quiet and perfect. Even though he was interviewing his dad, he wanted it to be formal and productive with no distractions. He checked his questions once more before beginning.

"Dad, I am anxious to hear what happened after Judge

Riker sent you to northern Nevada, but first, I must ask two questions, and I hope you will agree to answer both of them. The first question is about the night we were celebrating your birthday at the Branding Iron Restaurant, and during Nanna's speech, you ran out screaming about why she had abandoned you and that you wish you had not been born. Would you mind sharing what happened and why you said those things?"

"Yeah, that was a tough one," Terrance began. "First of all, let me be clear about the abandoned reference. I was not talking about your Nanna but about my biological mother. For whatever reason, I had been kind of melancholy all during that day. In fact, I tend to get that way a lot of times on my birthday as I start to reflect back on my life.

"Son, I love your Nanna with all my heart; in fact, I could not love her more. I also appreciate the fact that she and Dad did everything humanly possible to help me get my life back on track. But deep down, there has always been this yearning to find out about my biological mother.

"I was told that she died from an overdose the year after CPS took us away from her and put us in the foster care system. I think subconsciously I've always blamed her for what happened to me in the foster homes. I've wrestled with this problem most of my life, and even now when I have grown children of my own, I still wrestle with it. I try to wrap my head around why someone would get pregnant and then deliberately do things to harm that child.

"People have told me that she was probably addicted to drugs, and that it's not easy to stop doing them once addicted. I've even studied and talked to health professionals about the power of addiction, and that has helped me understand it a little better. Nevertheless, I still struggle.

"I think I am most bitter about the fact that even after I was born, and she was able to hold me, and see me, touch me, and tell me that she loved me, she still didn't seem to care. It seems like she didn't care enough about any of us to do what was necessary to keep us together as a family. By continuing to use the drugs and not care for us properly, she basically abandoned my siblings and me, and we ended up in the foster care system.

"Can you imagine how devastating a child feels when they think about the person who brought ... them ... in ... to this ... world ... just throwing them away like they're nothing? I guess I am bitter because I suffered through thirty-nine months of hell because of it. I continue to work on getting past the bitterness, for it's definitely not healthy. Perhaps in time, I will be able to completely forgive, although I doubt if I can ever forget."

They sat in silence for a few minutes because Michael felt that speaking to his dad immediately after would be almost intrusive. He had noticed that during the time his dad had been speaking, his hands went from resting in a relaxed manner on his legs to gripping his kneecaps so hard that his veins began to protrude.

The tense moments passed, and his dad was the first to break the silence. "Okay, son, what's the next burning question you have for me?"

Michael breathed a sigh of relief and continued. "Do you remember the night I asked you about the two round burns on your arm, and you said you got them as punishment for doing something wrong? What on earth did you do, and how did you get the scars?"

Terrance took his time, and it appeared he was trying to get his thoughts together and his nerves calm enough to begin. He began speaking softly and slowly as though he was afraid someone else would hear what he had to say.

"Son, I can't really give you specific details, but there are times when I have this flashback where a huge figure is towering over me. He is yelling and screaming while backing me into a corner and saying I must be punished for being a bad boy. The place where I am is real dark except for the glow from the cigarette he has in his mouth.

"I remember the glow getting brighter just before he removed it from his mouth and moved his hand holding the cigarette in my direction. I knew what was coming and let out the loudest scream I could possibly make. Suddenly, he hit me so hard across my face while at the same time he ground the cigarette into my arm.

"I must have blacked out at that point. Even though I was young, I remember the pain to his day. When I came to, I was in a closet lying on a pile of clothes. I could hardly move, and there was this weird smell which I now know that it was my arm. It gets kind of foggy after that, except I do remember Miss Addie putting some grease on the burn and telling me to say I got it when I ran into the radiator.

"You know, Michael, you'd think that after all these years, I would have forgotten about that incident, but I haven't. Do you remember a couple of summers ago when we had your

sister's graduation party in the backyard, and I was barbecu-
ing? Well, you probably don't remember, but right in the
middle of the party, I disappeared for about thirty minutes, and
John had to take over at the grill. Well, there was something
about the smell of the meat and the glowing embers beneath
that triggered a panic attack. I started hyperventilating and
could not continue. I practically ran into the bedroom, and I
tried to get away from everyone and regroup. The scene also
replays itself during many of my nightmares."

*"Oh, my goodness!" was all Michael could say as he sat
there shocked and trying to get his bearings. Then, suddenly,
he remembered,* That's why Dad woke up screaming and
drenched in sweat when he had the nightmare while we were
camping up near Mammoth Lakes, *he thought. Now, it all
started to make sense. Who knows? Maybe even cooking over
the campfire might have triggered it.*

*How could an adult do that to a child or even another
human being? The perpetrator had not only injured his dad
physically but mentally and emotionally as well. Here was his
dad almost forty years later, suffering the negative effects of
that horrendous act. All he could say was "Dad, I am so sorry.
I wish I could do more to take away the pain, but if it helps
any, I love you so much, and I am so proud that you are my
father."*

"Thanks, son, that really means a lot," Terrance responded.

*"Okay, Dad, now will you please share what happened to
you after Judge Riker sent you to northern Nevada instead of
letting you remain in southern California?"*

"Sure," Terrance responded, "I think what happened in
Nevada is probably one of the most important and pivotal

parts of my story. It is also difficult to talk about. Nevertheless, here goes.

"Little did I know that when they loaded me and several other guys into the van in San Bernardino and headed northeast for Nevada, that my world would soon be flipped on its head. The ride was long and boring, and the more we drove, the more desolate the terrain became.

"As we continued, each of the other guys was dropped off at different locations so that by the time we reached Sands Remote Desert Camp, which was where I would begin my Athletic Training Center program, I was the only one left. We arrived around three in the morning. It was dark, and I couldn't see a thing. The guy who came out to meet the van was this big burly dude who told me to get out and get my butt hauling inside.

"The room where they told me to go had one big glaring light bulb that hurt my eyes, and the same guy who met the van was now sitting at this little desk asking me a million questions. He started yelling at me and telling me to pay attention, but it was hard since I was still half asleep. He then did a search, I guess to make sure I didn't have any drugs on me.

"Next, he weighed me and checked for scars and bruises. Finally, he gave me a sheet, blanket, and pillow and took me to my room. There were four bunk beds with two upper and lower bunks. He told me to take the lower bunk bed by the window. I was told that I needed to be up by 6:00 and out on the road running by 6:30, and that I needed to aim for running the three miles in under twenty-eight minutes. What? That meant I would have less than three hours to get some sleep. I would later learn that the sleep issue would be the least of my concerns."

Michael's next question of why his dad had taken so many chances, risked getting hurt, and doing irreparable harm to himself and others brought about a gut-wrenching realization.

"You know, I didn't really care if I got hurt or not. All I was concerned about was how much I could get away with because it made me feel smart and like I was worth something. It gave me a sense of power and made me feel good for the time being. I only thought about myself and didn't care who else got hurt. Why should anyone else care about me? Apparently, subconsciously, I was still fending for myself like I had learned to do in the foster homes.

"If I didn't take care of me, then who else was going to do it? That's probably why I got into so many fights, regardless of whether I was in juvenile detention facility, group home, or at school. Because of my attitude, it took me almost two years to complete the nine-month program in Nevada. Let me explain.

"The program was set up in three sections, each to be completed in a three-month period. Anyone coming into the program was first sent to the Sands Remote Outpost located somewhere out in the middle of nowhere in the desert. This was the most strenuous of the three programs, and in retrospect, I think it was designed to break the rebellious spirit of those coming into it. Completion of the Sands phase was based on earning enough credits to be promoted to phase two and move to the Athletic Training Center.

"Because of my rebellious attitude, I would get to a certain point where I had earned a significant number of credits, then

I would either get into a fight or do something else stupid and lose all the credits I had earned up to that point. I had been there almost eleven months when I received a letter from Mom that caused my world to come crashing down. In fact, that letter was so earth-shattering to me that I still have it tucked away with other important papers, even though it was written twenty-seven years ago. In fact, instead of me trying to explain what was in the letter, give me a few minutes to get it, and I'll read it to you."

As Dad got up to go and retrieve the letter, Michael knew he was about to again witness seeing a side of his dad that he had never seen before today. Unfortunately, he was not able to tape his dad talking about the cigarette incident because it was far too personal and traumatic. However, he wanted to capture as much of this moment as he possibly could.

He used the time while his dad was gone to check his recording device to make certain it was ready to record every word and every voice inflection. He even considered pulling out his phone and videotaping it but felt it might be too invasive. He realized that this reading would be a melding of three generations: the words of his grandmother being read by her son to his son.

Terrance soon returned, removed the letter from the now-yellowed envelope, opened it, took a moment to compose himself, and began reading somewhat timidly:

September 8, 1989

.   .   .

My Dear Son,

I hope this letter finds you better than you were a couple of days ago. I received another call from Mr. Sage, the director there at the Sands Remote Camp, and unfortunately, he and the other staff members are disappointed that you are not making the progress they had hoped for.

It is my understanding that you are again on restricted activities because of your latest caper, or should I be a little more specific and say, your tomfoolery. Apparently, you didn't learn your lesson about trying to run away from the center a week or so ago. Even though the staff had taken your shoes away to keep you from trying to leave, you were determined to leave again anyway. Now, you are sitting there with blistered feet as well as recovering from heat stroke and dehydration. You were so anxious to get away that you gave no thought to running out into the desert in 100-plus degree temperature with no shoes, no hat, and no water. You are continuing to pull off the same old antics you did when you were home. You've just changed locations.

TJ, I strongly believe that you are trying to run away from your problems and the demons that seem to haunt you night and day. However, what you fail to realize is that you are your biggest problem, and even if you try to run away, you take your problems with you. As the old saying goes, "Everywhere you go, there you are."

There are several reasons why Judge Riker sent you to the Athletic Training Center in northern Nevada instead of to Los Padrinos or McLaren juvenile halls in southern California. Let me just take a minute here and remind you of those reasons.

First, because of Dr. Archer's expert testimony, Judge Riker gained some insight into what challenges you were facing because of your past negative experiences.

Second, as a result of Coach Wilson's testimony regarding how talented and gifted you are as an athlete, he felt that if anything would have even a ghost of a chance of rehabilitating you, it would be by placing you where you could develop that tremendous gift.

Third, as a result of my testimony regarding the abuse you experienced while in foster care, he agreed that much of your destructive and disruptive behavior could be an outward mani-festation of your anger and strong desire to retaliate. I don't know if you realize just how fortunate you are because most people who have similar arm-long lists of offenses like you do would never be given the opportunities that you have constantly been given. Yet you have managed to screw up every single one of those opportunities time and time again.

TJ, I regret to inform you that I am at the end of my rope, and so is your dad. From the minute you came into our lives up until now, we've done nothing but try to love and treat you like a son. You, on the other hand, have done everything humanly possible to treat us like dirt under your feet. You put forth extra effort to defy us at every turn, and you have made your sister cry so many times that I'm sure if we were counting, it would be in the triple digits by now. You go out of your way to be mean and inconsiderate, and everything, no matter how devastating and hurtful, is a game or a big joke to you. You have become increasingly insensitive, sarcastic, and selfish.

I pray for you every day, and I will continue to pray that you successfully complete the program. At this point, though, it is up to you to change your ways. While I wish you the best, I can no longer allow you to tear the family apart with your selfishness.

Please remember, I will always love you.

Sincerely,

·   ·   ·

Mom

Michael had noticed his dad's voice cracking and the couple of times he wiped away tears while reading the letter. He also noticed his dad's somber mood as he finished reading it, carefully refolding and placing it back into the envelope as though it was a precious jewel. Michael was reluctant to say anything but knew he eventually had to. He felt that this letter, in a substantial way, had brought about a significant change in his dad, and he had to know the why and what. After he allowed what he felt was an appropriate lapse of time, he posed this question to his dad.

"Dad, I noticed how quiet and reflective you became after reading the letter from Nanna. What was it about that letter that put you in a completely different mood?"

Without hesitation, Terrance began to explain. "Michael, up to that point, it had always been about me. For as long as I could remember, I had always put myself first. I was running away, stealing things, breaking other people's things, breaking into people's homes, duping the folks who were trying to help me, and making Dad and Mom spend money they didn't have just to make sure I got the help I needed.

"I simply didn't care. It was all fun and games to me. The more I was able to get away with things, the better and smarter I felt. In fact, many times, I surprised myself by what I had been able to get away with. To put it bluntly, I was out of control. I had even convinced myself that I didn't need help from anybody.

"Subconsciously, I think I just always expected Mom and

Dad to be there, regardless of what I did or how I treated, or perhaps I should say mistreated, them. Yet, if you had asked me, I would never have admitted it because that would show that I was dependent on someone besides myself, and I definitely couldn't have that.

"I was Mr. Big-Time TJ, totally independent and needing no one to make it through life. What I didn't realize, though, is that I had actually come to love and depend on my family, and the thought of not having them there ...

"When I received the letter, I had been at the Remote Camp for eleven months, although I was supposed to have only been there three months. Several times, I had earned almost enough credits and was so close to being promoted to the Athletic Training Center or ATC, but as usual, I would screw up and have to start all over again. It seemed like the more I screwed up, the more hostile and belligerent I became, which created a vicious cycle.

"I can remember two incidents in particular where I became almost like an insane person. The first incident happened when a kid in the program decided he would start harassing me by staring and mumbling things about me under his breath. This had been going on for a couple of weeks. Each time he would do it, I would tell him to turn around, stop staring at me, and mumbling under his breath about me. On this particular day, I was not in a good mood because I was missing home and feeling all alone.

"Unfortunately, I was still at the remote level, where my family was not allowed to come and visit because you were only allowed visits once you promoted to ATC. We were standing in line, and this kid was directly in front of me. He first began by halfway turning around, rolling his eyes, and turning back around to face the front. He did this several times, and I tried to ignore him.

"Apparently, he mistook my silence for weakness and felt emboldened to start turning all the way around and glaring at me. I told him to turn around and leave me alone. He did, then turned back around and glared at me again. I had had enough. Without realizing what I was doing, I grabbed him by the neck, slammed him onto the floor, and the next thing I knew, people were pulling me off him. I later found out that not only had I knocked out two teeth, but the guy had blacked out.

"The punishment I received for that act was extremely severe to put it mildly. I was taken and forced to spend a day on the platform. The platform was some boards nailed together that were about five-feet-wide and seven-feet-long and was placed out in the sun in the desert. I was forced to lie down on this platform and not get up until told to do so.

"It was extremely hot and uncomfortable, the temperature being above 100 degrees. After what seemed like an eternity, I started to get up when one of the guards came over, lifted me straight up above the boards, and slammed me back down on the searing platform so hard that I still carry the scar today from the injury I received.

"The second incident was the one Mom referred to in her letter. I had gotten into another altercation with a different kid in the program because he kept messing with my stuff. I caught him rummaging through my bag, and I uppercut him. His head snapped, and he fell against the wall, putting a dent in it. Later when the supervisor found out about me hitting the kid and damaging the wall, he said I would be on punishment for the next two days.

"I was so angry and ticked off about it that I took off running away without my shoes, hat, or water. Needless to say, I was forced to return to the camp in about an hour since I was not prepared to battle against the sun, the burning sand, and the 100-plus degree temperature. Would you believe I was only five credits from being eligible to promote to the next level? My attempt to run away put my credits back at zero.

"Apparently after that incident, one of the supervisors contacted Mom. It may have been due to policy that required them to notify your parents when you got sick or sustained a serious injury. I think they were concerned about the pretty serious burns on my feet and that I may have been suffering from heat stroke as well.

"You know, son, there was something about Mom's letter that stopped me dead in my tracks. Not only did I not want to lose my family, but all of a sudden, there were two reasons that were more important to me than just thinking about myself.

"First, I did not want to disappoint or embarrass Mom anymore. I thought back to the many times she had been there like a rock, refusing to listen to what other people were saying about how bad I was or how I was never going to amount to anything. They even told her she didn't have to put up with me but rather should just take me back to the adoption agency. Even some of her so-called friends and family members told her she should get rid of me and make me a ward of the state. I finally opened my eyes and realized that her unconditional love had been there since day one, and that I was one lucky dude to have a mother like that.

"The second reason was that I wanted to prove to my dad that I could make something of myself and not continue to be the thug and the loser who everyone said would most likely end up in prison. I also came to realize that my sister, Lynn, had gone out of her way to make sure I had a big sister I could always count on. I remember the summer she worked at a clothing store in the mall near our home. Every other week when she got paid, she would stop at stores in the mall and buy me clothes and games or come home and give me money so I could go to the arcade. Now, I was on the verge of losing it all.

"The following Monday after receiving Mom's letter, I was back running my qualifying three miles and coming in at 25.8 minutes. Since this was below the twenty-eight minute maximum time allowed, I began earning credits again. Three months from that day, I was promoted to level two and moved to the Athletic Training Center.

"My timing was perfect, for the athletic director, Mr. Vaughn, was in the process of putting together a track team that he planned to enter into local competitions. I asked to try out and after a week's time was selected as a member of the team to run the 4 x 100 relay. He also started helping me train to run the 100 and 200 meter dash. I guess all those days spent running at the remote camp site were finally going to pay off.

"Two weeks after I arrived at the ATC, Mom drove up from southern California and spent the entire day with me. It had been over a year since I had seen her, and I had to try hard to keep from crying. I was so happy to see her that I must have hugged her a million times and couldn't keep from grinning the entire time she was there. She had brought me some new clothes and a big bag of treats that included several packages of Twinkies®.

"The best treat of all, though, was her visit. It felt so good to have her stay for lunch and talk to the other guys at the ATC. Just before she got ready to leave, I told her I had a surprise. Then, I told her about being selected to be a member of the 4 x 100 relay team and that I was training to compete in the 100- and 200-meter dash and the long jump. She grabbed my hand, held it as tightly as she could, and smiled bigger than I had seen her smile in years as tears of joy welled up in her eyes. She kept saying, 'I knew you had it in you. I just knew it!' I felt like a million dollars and could not wait to be able to tell her how well I was doing on the track team.

"It had been a phenomenal season with us winning all the local track meets as well as meets as far away as Carson City, Minden, and Lake Tahoe. I remember as we were returning to the center following our final regular scheduled track meet, Coach Vaughn informed us that we had qualified to participate in the state track meet. We could not believe our ears, but it was also scary since we knew we would be competing with teams in the big league.

"On a beautiful spring day in April 1990, Mom and Dad drove up to the University of Nevada at Reno to attend the Nevada State Track and Field Meet. I can still remember them sitting in the stand rooting for me as I headed down the track running as fast as I could to come in second in the 100-meter dash and third in the 200-meter dash. I also placed in the top three for my long jump. In all but one event, my times and distance reflected my personal best. I think having my family there encouraged me to strive to do better than I had ever done up to that point.

"However, the highlight of the day was when we took to the track to run the 4 x 100 relay. During one of our qualifying runs the previous day, Chris had executed a bad hand-off to MC who dropped the baton. We all knew we were up against competition like we had never seen before, and we were visibly nervous.

"Some members from other teams started pointing, laughing, and talking badly about us, calling us the thugs from the prison school, which certainly did nothing to build our confidence. Our coaches took us off to the side and reminded us that talk was cheap, and that people who were insecure would stoop low enough to try to make others feel bad in order to boost their own self-esteem.

"Mr. Vaughn also reminded us that we had to have been good in order to make it to the state championship meet, and that all we had to do was go out and run the same as we had done at all the other meets that qualified us to be there. We left that little pep-talk meeting determined to show the world what we could do.

"Chris, chosen to run the first leg of the relay, was this kid from Fresno who reminded me a lot of myself. He had this incredible ability to get out of the block with lightning speed, giving us an edge right out the gate. Ordinarily, none of us would have been concerned about him running his leg, but he had been battling the flu all week and had seemed a bit sluggish on our last two qualifying runs.

"It was clear to all of us that he was struggling. Since our group was so small, we didn't have the luxury of backup runners, so we all had our fingers crossed that he would be back to the old Chris when we ran the finals that afternoon.

"I must say that running on a track like the one at the University of Nevada stadium was intimidating. We had never experienced anything like it. I didn't realize it then, but we must have looked like the little rag-tag team from Hicksville compared to some of our more well-heeled opponents, and in addition to talking about us to our faces, I'm sure they were rolling on the ground laughing behind our backs.

"We were all nervous, which certainly showed during our first practice run which was a complete disaster. However, we started looking better as we became more familiar with the track and began to focus on the job we had come to do, as our coaches kept reminding us."

"When our race was called, Chris took his place on the block in lane one, and when the starter's gun fired, he was off like a flash of light. *Looking good, l-o-o-k-i-n-g good!* I thought as he came into the exchange zone and handed off to MC. I took a deep breath and extended my right hand to receive the baton as MC came into the zone. Then, it was reach, grab, run! With legs pumping and heart pounding, I was off, running the race of my life.

"Rounding the curve, all I could think of was keep hauling and get that baton into Greg's hand, and WHAM, I did it! The handoff was perfect! Now, all I could do was hold my breath as I watched him run like I had never seen him run before.

"When Greg crossed that finish line first, far out in front of the rest of the field, the stadium went wild. Even people who were there for other teams began cheering for us, the underdogs.

"The announcer, who had been giving a leg-by-leg account of the relay, began yelling over the loudspeaker, 'Oh my goodness, what an upset! Can you believe it? This team has come out of nowhere and simply blown their opponents out of the water! If the board is correct, they also just set a new state record. Unbelievable! UN-BE-LIEV-A-BLE!!! What a run by this relay team from the Athletic Training Center. These kids had something to prove, and they certainly proved it this afternoon. Enjoy your victory lap, guys! You have certainly earned it.'

"When it finally hit me that we had actually won, Chris, Greg, and MC were already jumping up and down celebrating and had started running the victory lap. Meanwhile, I had fallen to the ground, hands over my eyes, trying to keep them from seeing the tears that were streaming down my face. I wiped them away as quickly as I could, jumped up, and ran across the field to catch and join them on the other side of the track to finish the victory lap.

"Earlier, I had located where Mom and Dad were sitting, and now as I looked up into the stand, I couldn't help but notice Mom jumping up and down and frantically waving her arms. She had a smile on her face, even bigger than the one she had when I told her I had made the track team. Meanwhile, Dad had a hand on each side of his face, holding it while shaking his head as if in total disbelief.

"Never in my life had I ever experienced anything like it. This was better than any feeling I had gotten from stealing something or duping somebody. It was a feeling of empowerment. This felt good, and the crowd clapping and yelling for us made it even better. Best of all, though, was the fact that Mom and Dad had been there to witness it. I would definitely give them my trophy to take back home, and for once, they could brag about something good I had done instead of having to hang their heads in embarrassment.

"At that moment, I knew I wanted to have many more of these kinds of moments, and that I was willing to work hard and do whatever it took to make it happen."

TWENTY-FIVE

Against All Odds

T errance, Jazmine, and Beetrice arrived a little past 6:00 that morning and took their places in the line which now stretched more than a city block and would undoubtedly triple in size by the time the gates opened at 7:30. The sun was already up, and a slight morning mist still hung in the air. Even though it was certain to get much warmer as the day progressed, most donned jackets, sweaters, or colorful scarves for warmth. Some, cradling cups of Star-bucks, chatted amongst themselves, while others turned to share friendly greeting and make small talk with those standing behind or in front of them. All had looked forward to this day for some time and were there for similar reasons. Today was the day to celebrate, support, and bask in the accomplishments of their loved ones.

The huge, wrought-iron gate swung open at exactly 7:31, and the line began inching forward. Though there were no signs or ushers asking those entering to be quiet or speak softly, there was a quiet and solemnness about the group as it entered the grounds and made its way toward the theater. Perhaps the attendees felt this was the type of occasion where one needed to be quiet and observant, to take it all in, to bask in the moment, and realize the significance of this once-in-a-lifetime experience.

As the theater began filling to capacity, it was obvious that this was an international celebration. One familiar with the native dress or uniform of countries around the world would immediately recognize attendees from Ethiopia, Bangladesh, China, Scotland, Nepal, Uganda, Nigeria, India, and Vietnam.

Meanwhile back at Eliot House, Michael sat on his bed reflecting. He had worked, waxed, wangled, and withstood, waiting for this day to finally arrive. His black robe was draped over the back of his computer chair in such a way that the rising sun caught each fold, casting shadows of hills and valleys against the wall. Yes, there had been many highs and lows, struggles and victories these past four years, but the highs far out-numbered the lows. Who would have ever imagined the many firsts he had been able to accomplish?

Promptly at 9:59, trumpets resounded throughout the theater, signaling the beginning of the procession of Harvard's 365th commencement. At 10:00 sharp, Terrance, Jazmine, and Beetrice watched in awe as the commencement pageantry began. With the undergraduates lined up on each side and Harvard University's president leading the way, officers wearing tall black hats, dignitaries, and faculty members draped in hoods and stoles of many hues began making their way into Tercentenary Theater.

What a spectacular and colorful entry. Following behind

the faculty and graduate students were hundreds of black-robed undergraduates filing to their seats. These three were witnessing history in the making.

Soon, the program was underway with introductions, musical selections, and student speeches ranging from how the bite of a poisonous spider had led to the student's chosen career path to a motivational speech encouraging graduates to embrace and celebrate their uniqueness rather than apologizing for it. Beetrice's heart was pounding and head spinning as she tried to take in every single second of this once-in-a-lifetime experience.

Her facial muscles ached from the continuous ear-to-ear smile, and if she didn't stop pinching herself, her arm would be black and blue. Glancing to her left, she saw the proud faces of Terrance and Jazmine, and her heart leaped and rejoiced at this milestone which, twenty-seven years before, would not have even been imaginable. It almost seemed surreal, and she felt like she was on emotional overload. Little did she know that the best was yet to come.

Following the morning commencement exercise and the awarding of diplomas after lunch, the trio along with Michael headed back to Eliot House for a few hours of rest and relaxation before setting out to attend the grand finale, a happy hour and five-course dinner at Michael's fraternity house. Once they were settled at Michael's apartment, he set up his laptop and stated that he had a surprise for them. For the next hour, they sat transfixed as they watched the video.

The video began with a gentleman addressing a group of what appeared to be around 300 people seated around dinner tables that included younger and older adults, as well as some teenagers. He began by thanking them for their attendance, their contributions, their dedication to their communities, and to the organization.

He continued, "You all are in for a real treat, a fitting way to end our delicious meal and a highly successful fundraising drive. Tonight, we have as our guest speaker a young man who has become a legend in the greater Boston area. If any of you watched the final game last December between the rivals, Harvard and Yale, that is famously known as 'The Game,' you can't help but remember the nail-biting ending and the play this young man made in the final fifty-seven seconds. His unbelievable catch and sprint into the end-zone broke the tie and helped Harvard go on to win their third back-to-back Ivy League Championship.

"Over the course of his four years at Harvard, he has made outstanding contributions to the team, setting several records in the process and becoming the recipient of numerous awards. With his graduation just six weeks away, we didn't want to lose the opportunity to take advantage of having him speak to us since so many students leave the area once they graduate. So, without further delay, let's give a welcoming round of applause as I proudly present to you Mr. Michael Ferguson."

Good Evening Ladies and Gentlemen. It is with great pleasure that I stand before you this evening. Several months ago, I was assigned a class project that led to me doing some extensive research into my family's history, and the results both shocked and inspired me. So, this evening, I am going to be sharing with you some very personal information that I hope will be encouraging, informative, and uplifting as well as offer some life-lesson tenets.

I remember when I got my first college assignment back from my sociology professor. I received a B- for what I believed was one of the best academic papers I had written in a long time. Confused and disgruntled, I marched into my professor's office and asked why I had received a B- when I so clearly deserved an A.

She calmly responded, "Michael, I want to tell you a secret."

Confused but eager to hear what she had to say, I responded, "What's the secret?"

She said, "The paper could have been better, this is true, but the reason I gave you a B- is because so few people who get into this school have ever experienced failure, experienced defeat, experienced what it feels like to get a grade lower than an A. Everyone here considers himself to be brilliant, and most have received straight A's since grade school. Only a few have truly struggled or experienced disappointment.

• • •

"You see, the reason graduates are able to be so successful after departing from this university is because somewhere along the way, they learned how to respond to failure. They have learned how to get back up after being knocked down and how to come back determined to perform even better. That is why I gave you that grade. Now, how are you going to respond?"

*It wasn't until I had completed my family history assignment that I truly understood what my sociology professor was trying to teach me four years ago. You see, there's a theme that emerges after studying how people become successful. Look at the story of Chris Gardner, made famous by the 2006 biographical film **The Pursuit of Happyness**. In it, Will Smith portrays the life of a homeless salesman who, through hard work and determination, eventually lands a coveted role as a stockbroker.*

*There is one thing that remains true regardless of the profession, industry, or role that a successful individual holds. This message is as true today as it was almost 2,000 years ago when Julius Cesar sailed with his armada to the Cliffs of Dover only to set his army's ships on fire. He did this for the sole purpose of instilling in his soldiers the same message that I'm here to share with you today. **"When you make success the only possible outcome, there is no limit to how much you can achieve."***

.   .   .

Seventy-five years ago, my great-grandmother was poisoned to death. Her one-day-old baby, my grandmother, was also poisoned. The doctors gave her only three days to live, and if by some miracle she did live past the three days, the prognosis was that she would never be able to live a normal life due to the damage done by the poison. Yet today, she is alive and healthy, living a successful and highly productive life, and making a positive difference in the lives of others.

From 1973 until sometime in 1988, my dad went through a tumultuous period that few of you will ever experience. He was placed in foster care around four months of age, and remained there for the next thirty-nine months. During that time, he was abused, tortured, abandoned, and neglected, not just in one home but in several different homes. In 1976, he was adopted. Although he was fortunate to end up with a loving family who did everything they possibly could to try to eradicate the effects of the negative experiences he had suffered prior to the adoption, the damage had already been done.

For the next twelve years, my dad manifested signs of that abuse in every way imaginable. This included destroying property, rejecting lov,e and not allowing anyone to get close to him, disrupting any classroom or meeting he was attending, inflicting self-harm, fighting and disrespecting others, rejecting authority, and lashing out any way and every way he could.

. . .

As he moved into his early teens, this behavior escalated when he went from stealing things from home, stores, churches, and schools, to stealing cars, firearms, and the likes. Even though his adopted parents went out of their way to make sure he received mental health assessments, counseling, and therapy sessions, they seemed to have no positive effect on his disruptive and destructive behavior. Many people said he was a hopeless case and advised his parents to give up on him because he would never amount to anything in life. Yet he, too, defied all odds.

His tremendous accomplishments over the past twenty-six years have proven that when you strive to make success the only possible outcome and failure is not an option, there is no limit to what you can achieve.

But what is success? While working on this project, I looked up the definition of success and was disappointed at what I found. You see, success is tough to define. It has many definitions that vary in nature. Success has been defined as the accomplishment of an aim or purpose or the attainment of popularity or profit. Other definitions include "a person or thing that achieves desired aims or attains prosperity, or the fact of getting or achieving wealth, respect, or fame." So, it turns out, success is not defined by a singular definition.

. . .

Success is not tangible; it is not something that we can see, touch, or point to and say, "There it is!" Success is something that cannot be defined, but the evidence of its existence can be found in the history of those who have achieved it. Success is not an evaluation of your current position but rather an assessment of how far your current position is from where you started.

There is, however, one other ingredient necessary to succeed. Not only do you have to make success the only possible outcome, but you must also have a strong reason as to why you want to be successful. An individual striving for success without a clearly defined reason is as lost as a ship at sea with no compass or stars to guide it. My father was, to put it simply, a trouble-maker. He was defiant and reckless and did everything he could do to cause trouble. After so many attempts to change his behavior, my grandparents nearly gave up.

As he was going through a program designed to turn his behavior around, my grandmother wrote a letter to him that changed his life. She shared with him the pain and grief he had caused their family, while all they were trying to do was love him unconditionally. For the first time, he realized how his selfishness and self-centeredness were hurting the very people he did not want to hurt.

. . .

*This letter changed my father's life, not because it told him that he should turn his life around. His therapists, teachers, counselors, and program officers had told him this time and time again. This letter changed my father's life because it showed him **why** he should turn his life around. It made him realize that he should make the change not for himself but for his family, for those who had shown him nothing but love and support, and for those who would give anything to see him succeed. My father already had the potential to be successful; he was simply missing his **why**. The letter provided the reasons why he should turn his life around, why he should make better decisions, why he should make success the only possible outcome.*

*Once he discovered his **why**, he was unstoppable. It lit a fire beneath him that propelled him to heights he never thought attainable. He was determined to prove wrong everyone who said he would never amount to anything. Likewise, he wanted to show his family that they were right for believing in him, for supporting him when no one else did, and for loving him before he had learned to love himself.*

*After finding his **why**, my father went on to break state records in track and to win a state championship in football. He worked his way up from entry-level position to vice president at a well-known and highly respected firm. He not only raised five kids, four of whom are either in college or are college graduates, but taught each one the lessons he had learned that* *helped him succeed against all odds. He taught me the importance of hard work and determination and helped me hone my football skills.*

As previously mentioned, those who are football fans and know of the rivalry between Harvard and Yale may remember when I was able to score that game-winning touchdown in the last fifty-seven seconds to defeat the Yale Bulldogs in 'The Game' of 2015 and help Harvard win the Ivy League title. My dad now dedicates his life to helping other kids achieve success in athletics and in the classroom, encouraging them to believe in themselves, and helping them avoid the pitfalls that he experienced. He has also been recognized for his work with civic organizations and made it possible for numerous young people to get scholarships to attend college.

Vince Lombardi, one of the all-time greatest coaches once said, "The difference between a successful person and others is not a lack of strength, nor a lack of knowledge, but rather a lack of will.' Estee Lauder, one of the most influential business women to date said, 'I never dreamed about success—I worked for it.' And Albert Einstein, one of the most profound minds this world has ever witnessed said, "Genius is 1% talent and 99% hard work." He also said, "You have to learn the rules of the game, and then you have to play better than anyone else." Well, the rules of the game are simple. Whether you want to be an athlete, a coach, an entrepreneur, a scien-

tist, a doctor, a politician, or a college graduate, you must work hard for it.

As most of you may well know, it takes hard work, dedication, commitment beyond imagination, and an unwavering desire to do whatever it takes to be successful. However, there are some of you present in the audience tonight that are just getting started, and you need to understand that you are surrounded by people who want to see you succeed.

The advice and guidance of those who share it should not fall on deaf ears but should be valued and applied to the way you live your life. You must work hard and take advantage of every opportunity that is presented to you. There will be times when you experience difficult circumstances, there will be ups and downs, times when you feel on top of the world, untouchable, unbeatable, and times when all you want to do is give up.

Understand that every successful person has had these experiences. The difference between those who failed and those who overcame is how they let the tough times affect them. Those who overcome embrace the struggles and the failures because they understand that they are necessary in order to succeed.

One of my favorite quotes is by Michael Jordan. He said, "I have missed over 9,000 shots in my career. I've lost over 300 games. Twenty-six times, I've been trusted to take the game-winning shot and missed. I have failed over, and over, and over again in my life, and that is why I succeed."

If you can remember only one thing from me this evening, I hope it is this: I believe in each and every one of you. I know that you all have the potential to do great things and are capable of achieving your goals if you put in the work. It will not be easy. Your will and determination will be tested every day, but if you believe in yourself, embrace the ups and downs, the struggles and strife, and work hard day in and day out, you will be successful. Though we may not know how to define success, we do know what it takes to achieve it.

The reason I've shared my father's story today is first to let him know how integral he was in shaping me into the person that I am today. The second reason is to share with you the importance of passing on the lessons I have learned to the next generation. As in the case of my father, it may have been diffi-cult for others to believe that he had much potential at all or to visualize his life's trajectory.

But remember this: you can never tell what greatness lies within a person simply by looking at their outward appear-ance or their present behavior. From a different perspective, it may be difficult to convince others to believe in you. It may also be difficult to visualize your own life trajectory or to see your full potential. However, this is why you must always believe in yourself.

As I said, success is something that cannot be defined, but the evidence of its existence can be found in the history of those who have achieved it. It is only after we look back that we can see how far we have come. Success is not about where you've been or how disadvantaged your beginning but rather where you are going and what you set your mind to achieve. Believe you can achieve, even when others say you can't.

*In closing, I ask you to reflect back on the life of my dad, Terrence Ferguson, who was able to succeed against all odds after finding his **why**. As you face your daily challenges, I encourage you to strive in your quests to succeed, look to leave your mark in this world, and seek to provide mentorship and guidance so others can follow in your footsteps.*

If I may ask this of you, especially since this is being recorded, because so much of my speech focused on my dad, and since he was unable to be here tonight because he lives in California, would you please join me in giving a round of applause for him so that he will understand just how much of a positive impact he has had on my life and the lives of so many others?

In response to Michael's request, the audience rose to their feet and gave a standing ovation that lasted at least a full minute.

The video ended, and for a while, no one moved or made a sound. It wasn't until a while later that Beetrice noticed the tears flowing down Terrance's face. Unlike the time when his track team had won the 4 X 100 relay and he hid the tears from his teammates, this time, Terrance let the tears flow unabashedly as he fully realized the miracles that had been taking place in his life over the past twenty-seven years. He could not believe how his life had turned out and how he had positively impacted the lives of so many others. Beetrice reached for his hand, covered it with her other hand, and gave it an understanding squeeze.

While still holding Terrance's hand, Beetrice softly said a prayer of thanksgiving, and thought, Yes, Neiomi, you were right. Little Bee, as you so endearingly called me, is experiencing a blessed and miracle-filled life. To God be the Glory!"

Acknowledgments

A heartfelt thank you to all who made writing this memoir possible. Special thanks to those listed below who went above and beyond.

Glenn Fischer, for helping to make this story possible.

Timothy Fischer, for providing pertinent and accurate details for this book.

Minister Timothy Galvin, for your contribution and invaluable spiritual guidance.

Andrew Fischer, for your contribution and the eloquent way you pulled all the pieces together.

Dr. Toni S. Walters, for believing in and resurrecting this writing project, then dedicating many, many hours to reading and editing the manuscript.

Anita Miller-Clay, for being an invaluable resource and providing guidelines for rewrites.

Carmelita Brown, for your encouragement starting years ago as I contemplated writing this memoir.

Nadra Redding, for being my unofficial advisor and an unbelievably resourceful "sounding board."

Diane Nine of Nine Speakers, Inc., for your constructive suggestions and encouragement, even when the future looked bleak.

Steen of Steen Productions, for your constant encouragement and prayers

Sherri Kenny, for book promotion assistance.

Elvera Borders, for your continuous support, encouragement, and providing a quiet environment during the long writing process.

Diane Oberstein, for your suggestions and many hours of editing early in the project.

Johnny Green, for enabling me to get started on my writing journey.

Deborah Garner, for your encouragement and financial support.

Nathan Galvin, for your encouragement and financial support.

Matthew Ludwig, for financial support.

About the Author

Essie Knowles Fischer is an abuse survivor, the mother of an abuse victim, and an advocate for the abused. From a young age, she became interested in helping others because she knows personally the importance of having the support of a caring family, friends, advocates, and great teachers. As a music and language arts teacher in Chicago and Boston, she encouraged her students, many who were abuse victims, to use the mediums of music and writing to express themselves and for cathartic purposes.

As a middle and high school educator in multiple communities in both Utah and California, Essie introduced music therapy to help students with specific physical, emotional, and psychological disabilities. These programs offered experiences many of the students never thought they would have. In 2003, Essie was honored with California State's Educator of the Year award by the California League of Middle Schools.

After retiring as a public-school teacher, Essie became a mentor teacher for Glencoe McGraw Hill Publishers and later an educational consultant for Holt, Rinehart, and Winston Publishers. Her memoir, *Sinister Hands and Peachtree Miracles,* brings attention to the epidemic-proportioned problem of child abuse. It also provides hopeful direction for those working with the abused and encouragement to victims trying to overcome the negative impact abuse has had on their lives and their futures.

Essie currently lives in Georgia where she teaches private piano and voice lessons. Additionally, she runs an online business that focuses on spiritual and life experiences journaling, and genealogy research and scrapbooking. She also makes time to assist with the online service of Temple of Faith International Church in the Atlanta area and hopes to help the church establish a youth mentoring program. In her spare time, Essie loves reading, scrapbooking, and visiting her children and grandchildren who are spread throughout the United States.

Contact Information and Resources

Are you interested in

• Attending workshops hosted by the author?
• Having the author speak at an event?
• Being involved in teacher-training seminars on identifying and working with students who are abuse victims?
• Attending abuse victims workshops?
• Receiving free periodic newsletters with notices of upcoming events and updated information on relevant topics?
• Having the author participate in interviews?
• Participating in author-conducted Question and Answer sessions and sharing ideas with others?

Go to

• Author's website, **thecreativevisionaries.com**,
• click on "**contact**,"

• enter your name and email address and any other information you want to share.

or

• email the author at thecreativevisionaries2@gmail.com

You will be added to our mailing list.
Thank you for your interest!

Other resources below:

Childhelp National Child Abuse Hotline (800) 4-A-Child (800) 422-4453
National Abuse Hotline SafeHorizon (800) 621-4673
National Sexual Abuse Hotline (800) 656-4673
National Suicide Prevention Lifeline (800) 273-8255